10/1

NEW WORLD

3

FROM GALILEE TO ROME

NEW WORLD

3
From Galilee to Rome

by
ALAN T. DALE

OXFORD UNIVERSITY PRESS
1966

Oxford University Press, Ely House, London W.1

GLASGOW NEW YORK TORONTO MELBOURNE WELLINGTON
CAPE TOWN SALISBURY IBADAN NAIROBI LUSAKA ADDIS ABABA
BOMBAY CALCUTTA MADRAS KARACHI LAHORE DACCA
KUALA LUMPUR HONG KONG

Colour illustrations 5–8 by
BERNARD BRETT, FSIA

Colour illustrations 1–2 by
Leicestershire schoolchildren,
and 3–4 by
Israeli schoolchildren

FILMSET BY BAS PRINTERS LIMITED, WALLOP, HAMPSHIRE
AND PRINTED IN GREAT BRITAIN AT THE UNIVERSITY PRESS, OXFORD
BY VIVIAN RIDLER, PRINTER TO THE UNIVERSITY
COLOUR PLATES PRINTED IN HOLLAND BY VAN LEER AND CO., N.V.

Foreword

by the Rev. Canon C. F. D. Moule,
Lady Margaret's Professor of Divinity in the University of Cambridge

I REGARD Mr. Dale as a wizard, and I wish I knew the secrets of his art. He takes phrases from the New Testament, which, to me, are extremely familiar, because I happen to have studied them all my life, and he holds them up at a particular angle or gives them just a little tilt, and suddenly they shine with a new lustre and freshness. I say to myself, 'But is that really what it means?'; and when I ponder over it, I generally have to admit, 'Yes, of course, it is; but I had never looked at it like that before'. Mr. Dale has something of a poet's imagination, combined with an extremely practical and realistic way of asking 'What were things really like?' and a genius for the apt modern analogy. He has evidently thought so deeply about the meaning of New Testament words and ideas that he is able to paraphrase freely without losing the essentials.

A poet's vision; a realist's grasp of facts; and, we must add, a parent's understanding of the family. For this, too, makes him an effective interpreter. He knows his boys and girls so well that he can not only give them the story in lively, contemporary shape, but also suggest things for them to do, which will help them to think out the meaning of the Christian story for themselves and begin to make it their own.

It is remarkable how large a proportion of the New Testament is retained in these racy paraphrases and modernized presentations. From unexpected angles and in clever disguises, it comes back at the reader and startles him with its freshness and relevance.

I count it a privilege to be allowed to write this little foreword to volumes which, I am sure, are going to help to kindle genuine reverence for Jesus Christ and to show readers how real and contemporary the Gospel is.

Clare College,
Cambridge.

5

from the Preface

Here, in these five books, we can read the story of Jesus and his friends. We have called them *New World*, for this is the story of how God made clear to us what he is like and what he is doing, and called us to help him in building a real world.

In *The Beginning* you can see what Jesus was like and how he lived in God's Way.

In *The Message* you can listen to Jesus himself, explaining God's Way and making it clear.

In *From Galilee to Rome* you can see how his friends carried on the work he began in Galilee, and how, as they went out into the world, they began to see more clearly what he had lived and died for.

In *Paul the Explorer* you can see what Jesus meant to one man. Paul had never met Jesus in Galilee as Peter had done; he became a Christian some four or five years after the death of Jesus. But this is what, in his own words, Jesus meant to him: 'God, who made this bright world, has filled my heart with light, the light which shines now that I know what he is really like. This was the light shining from the face of Jesus.' He set out to tell the Good News all over the world.

These four books tell the story of Jesus and his friends. We must now look back at the whole story and ask 'What did Jesus mean to his friends?' 'What did they think about him?' 'Who did they think he was?' Two friends of Jesus can help us here—Paul, whose story we have already told, and the friend who wrote the Fourth Gospel (*John*) in Ephesus about A.D. 100. They explain how Jesus helped them to know what God is like and to live in his Way, to understand the world in which they were living and to live splendidly in it. Jesus was their Leader—and more than their Leader; he was their Lord. In *Jesus Leader and Lord* you can read what they had to say. They can help us to find out what Jesus can mean to us, and how we too can learn to 'live splendidly' in our very different twentieth-century world.

Contents

List of Illustrations

Peter and John healing the Cripple at the gate of the Temple, by Rembrandt
(*British Museum*). A note about Rembrandt can be found in *Jesus—Leader
and Lord*.   *end papers*

The publishers would like to thank the *Leicestershire Education Committee*, and the
Israeli Embassy, London for the help they have given in finding the children's paintings
reproduced in this book.

You, who are my friends, must be like salt; you must make the whole life of the world worth living.

Your business will be to go all over the world to tell everybody what you know about me. You must go . . . to the very ends of the earth.   Jesus

Jesus has broken down all barriers. He is all that matters and he is changing the whole life of the world.   Paul

The Background

In *The Beginning* and *The Message* we have listened to the story of Jesus as his friends remembered it: what he did, and what he said to the people in the villages and to his friends.

Jesus had lived all his life in Palestine. Only once had he crossed the borders of his native land to live for a few months in a foreign country and in the mountains north-east of Galilee. He had wanted to be alone with his friends after the men of the Resistance Movement had tried to make him their 'king' at the Desert Meal. Then he had gone to the southern parts of his native land to tell the Good News of God there, as he had done in Galilee in the north. After about six months he had been caught one night in an orchard, and executed.

He had spent his time talking to his own people. There were large Greek cities in Palestine, one not far from Nazareth; but we do not hear of his going to any of them and talking to the foreigners there about the Good News. He chose to live in the small villages talking to his own people, and he told his friends that they were to do the same while they were with him.

Yet Jesus did not come just to tell the Good News to Jewish people; the Good News, he believed, was for the world. 'When everybody everywhere throughout the world lives in God's Way, people will come from north, south, east and west and sit down at supper together.'

This is a tremendous task, and Jesus knew it. Indeed, today, twenty centuries after Jesus lived, we are only beginning to see how tremendous it is.

Jesus believed that, if the Good News was to be told to everybody everywhere, his own people—the Jewish people—must first see what the Good News really means; then the Jewish people could tell the world. He believed that *his* work was to deal only with his own people.

But we must never forget, as Jesus did not forget, that the Good News was not just for the Jewish people; it could not be. It was Good News for everybody everywhere—or it was Good News for nobody.

UNDERSTANDING JESUS

Jesus believed that, since the Good News was for the whole world, he needed friends to help him.

We have seen, in *The Beginning*, how Jesus gathered a group of friends round him. Some went on living and working in their own villages; a small group of close friends, the 'Twelve', left their homes and lived with him and shared his travels. After the Desert Meal, when he refused to have anything to do with the Resistance Movement, most of his friends left him. He was not the sort of man they had thought he was.

His close friends stuck by him. They loved him too much to leave him. But they, too, did not understand him, and sometimes Jesus had to talk severely to them. 'You're not thinking of what God wants,' he said to them. 'You're talking like everybody else.' Sometimes *they* tackled *him* and asked him the strangest questions. In the orchard, at the end, they all ran away.

But it was not easy to understand Jesus. This was not because he did not talk plainly; he did. But he was talking about something bigger than they had ever dreamed of—about a world in which all men are equal in God's sight and must live as members of one family, God's Family. It is hard to think of foreigners as equals and brothers, especially if we live in an occupied country and foreign soldiers are our masters; or if we have never met foreigners in their homeland (where *we* are the foreigners) and do not understand their point of view.

Understanding Jesus takes time.

His friends understood him so little that, when he died, they thought it was all over. Only when, to their amazement, he was raised to life again, did they begin to see that the story was by no means over; indeed, it had only just begun.

Even then, they did not understand all that was in his heart. They had to find out the hard way. Only when they began to cross the borders of Palestine and live in other countries and meet foreigners as friends, did they really begin to understand all that Jesus had lived and died for.

It was the overseas friends of Jesus who understood him best.

Dr. Luke was a foreigner himself, and he knew that, if we want to understand Jesus, we must read more than the story of what happened in Palestine. We must see what happened afterwards in the countries beyond it. For it is all one story.

From Galilee to Rome tells this wider story in the words of Dr. Luke. His story begins, as Mark's does, in Galilee, but it ends, not in Jerusalem City, the capital of the Jewish nation, but in Rome, the capital of the Roman Empire—the capital, as people said, of the 'inhabited world'.

THE WIDER STORY

The Beginning is the story of Jesus; *From Galilee to Rome* is the story of Jesus and his friends.

We begin in Palestine, and look again at the story we read in *The Beginning*, but this time from a different point of view.

In *The Beginning* we saw what happened between the Call of Jesus by Jordan River and the tremendous moment, on that first Easter Sunday, when his friends met Jesus again and knew that not even death could conquer him.

In *The Message* we saw what Jesus said and how he said it.

Now, as we tell the story again—but with different stories about Jesus from Dr. Luke's notebook—we shall try to find out *why* he lived and talked as he did in Galilee and Jerusalem. We must see more clearly what he was trying to do. For we know now that this is only the first part of a wider story.

The second part of the story—the next thirty or forty years—is the story of what the friends of Jesus did after that first Easter Sunday. This story begins in Jerusalem City, goes out into Palestine (we shall find ourselves in Samaria and on the Desert Road to Egypt), then across the world (through the highlands of Anatolia and the cities on the shores of the Aegean Sea) to Rome, the capital of the Roman Empire.

The real story of Jesus, as Dr. Luke saw it, is a world story. We shall meet all sorts of people—people of great ports and highland towns, farmers and sailors and merchants and craftsmen. We shall find ourselves in riots in city streets and in a great storm between the island of Crete

13

and the quicksands of the African coast. The people speak Greek or their own strange native languages. We shall travel along the great Roman roads and in large Egyptian grain-ships. And at the end we shall walk along a famous Roman road, the Appian Way, into Rome itself.

In all these far-off places we shall hear the friends of Jesus telling the Good News in the great cities of the world, as Jesus did in the villages of Galilee. They talk about Jesus and tell people why they are his friends. Nothing less than the whole world is big enough for Jesus.

Dr. Luke and his Notebook

We should have known nothing of this wider story if Dr. Luke had not become a friend of Jesus—and kept a notebook.

We wish we knew more about Dr. Luke himself—'my doctor', as Paul called him. He may have come from North Africa—he was a 'foreigner' not a Jew—but probably his home was Antioch where (as you will read) the great plan to tell the Good News to people all over the world was made. He was certainly a townsman, not a countryman like Jesus. Afterwards he went to Macedonia; it was while he was there that Paul came down to the town of Troas, on the coast of Asia opposite Macedonia. Dr. Luke went over to Troas to meet Paul and beg him to come over into Europe. (Was he the 'man from across the water, a Macedonian' Paul saw in his dream? see *Paul the Explorer*.) Paul went across the water to Macedonia; and when he left Philippi City in Macedonia he left Dr. Luke to look after the friends of Jesus there. Paul came back to Philippi City, and Dr. Luke joined him on his last journey to Palestine and on the long sea voyage, through the autumn storms, to Rome itself.

He kept a notebook. Into his notebook he put stories about Jesus which he picked up during the two years he spent with Paul in Palestine. He also asked people what had happened in the early days after that first Easter Sunday, and jotted down what they told him. And into his notebook he put his diary. (We can tell when he uses his diary in his book, because, when he is using it, he writes 'we', not 'they'.)

Many years after Paul's death, when Dr. Luke was living in Greece he sat down to write a full account of Jesus and his friends for His Excellency Theophilus. (You can read what he told Theophilus about his book on pp. 16 and 47.) He had his notebook and his diary. He also had a copy of Mark's story of Jesus and a 'Book of the Sayings of Jesus'. From these sources he made his book.

Dr. Luke had so much to tell His Excellency Theophilus that he filled two volumes before his story ended: the first volume told the story of Jesus; the second volume told how the friends of Jesus took the Good News from Jerusalem to Rome. We call them here 'Part One' and 'Part Two'.

We have already used Mark's story and Dr. Luke's 'Book of the Sayings of Jesus' in *The Beginning* and *The Message*. We shall not use them again here. We shall take the stories from Dr. Luke's notebook, for most of these are stories we have not yet heard. But, in this book, we shall not use all the stories Dr. Luke jotted down in his notebook and diary. Many of them are about Paul; we shall save these for the next book, *Paul the Explorer*. Paul was so important a friend of Jesus that he must have a book to himself.

Part One—The Pioneer

We do not know who Theophilus was, except what we can learn from this letter. He seems to have been an important person; Roman governors were addressed as 'Your Excellency'. He may have been a Christian.

Many people have tried to write the story of what has happened among those of us who are the friends of Jesus; they used the reports which those who met Jesus face to face have handed down to us.

I thought that I too, Your Excellency, would try to write the story down. For some time now I have been trying to find out what actually happened, and I will put it down in its proper order. I want you to know the truth of what has been told to you.

Luke

Right: THE DEMENTED TOMB DWELLER. This picture has been painted by Adrienne Abbott, aged 11, of Heathfields High School, Earl Shilton, Leicester. You will find the story she has painted in *The Beginning*, page 34.

16

The story of Jesus that Dr. Luke tells us is the same story that Mark told. But he tells it in a different way; he wants us to see from the very beginning *why* Jesus lived as he did, something his friends were very slow to learn. Indeed, he wants us to see *how* his friends came at last to understand what he wanted them to do.

He wants us to see that Jesus is Lord as well as Leader, one to whom we can give our whole hearts and the service of our lives, and who gives us God's power—God's Spirit in our hearts—so that we can live in God's Way. Jesus is everybody's Lord.

Dr. Luke was not born in Palestine and he was not a Jew, as we have seen; he came from one of the great cities of the Roman Empire. It was an amazing thing, he felt, that Jesus cared for *him*—and people like him— as well as for his own fellow-countrymen like Peter. And it was not just that Jesus cared for everybody everywhere, whatever their race or the colour of their skin; what amazed Dr. Luke was the way Jesus cared especially for people nobody else bothered with.

How could he, then, tell the story of Jesus as if it was just a story of something that happened in Palestine? It was a story for the whole world about the whole world.

This is just where the friends of Jesus come in. His Galilean friends were only the first members of a great company of friends who were to spread all over the world. They did not realize this at first; but Dr. Luke wants us to see that this was why Jesus called them—and why he calls us to be his friends today.

What Dr. Luke also could not forget was what the love of Jesus cost Jesus himself. He faced death itself because he cared for everybody everywhere. Those last few days show us how great his love was.

The story begins by Jordan River, and Part One of his book ends in a capital city—Jerusalem. But this is not the end of the story (as the friends of Jesus thought at the time); it is only the beginning. So Part One of Dr. Luke's story is only the story of what Jesus *began* to do and to teach, as he told His Excellency Theophilus.

Left: ZACCHAEUS IN THE TREE. This picture has been painted by Priscilla Mary Makovsky, aged 9, of Barkby Parochial Primary School, Leicester. You will find the story she has painted in *From Galilee to Rome*, page 33.

Dr. Luke's story begins, as Mark's did, with the story of John the Hermit and the Call of Jesus by Jordan River. It is the year A.D. 27, and the Emperor Tiberius had been ruling the Roman Empire for fifteen years.

Dr. Luke tells us more about John the Hermit than Mark did. He describes the sort of man he was and what he said to the people.

Most of all Dr. Luke wants us to see what his Call meant to Jesus. Jesus had come to join John's company of friends to get ready for the coming of God's Chosen Leader. Jesus now knew that God had called *him* to be the Chosen Leader. He had to think through again what sort of Leader God wanted him to be. He made his great decision and left the moorlands to be a wandering teacher, talking to people in their villages and meeting them as equals.

John the Hermit

In the year A.D. 27—the fifteenth year of the reign of the Emperor Tiberius—Pilate was the Governor of Judea; King Herod and his brother Philip and King Lysanius were ruling princes in the countries to the north and east; and Annas and Caiaphas the High Priests were the Leaders of the Jewish people. However, it was to John the Hermit, out on the moorlands, that God spoke.

Now John had gone out to the banks of Jordan River and was calling people to change their ways so that God might forgive them.

He was like the man in the old poem in the Bible—

> The voice of a man
> Shouting in the lonely desert—
> 'Get God's road ready,
> Make his paths straight.'
> Every valley shall be filled up,
> Every mountain and hill be levelled out,
> Winding roads made straight,
> Rough roads made easy.
> Everybody shall see God coming to our help.

Crowds went out to be baptized by John in Jordan River as a

sign that they had changed their ways.

'You are like poisonous snakes,' John told them. 'Who told you to escape from the terrible times that are coming? If you've really changed your ways, you must show it in the way you live. You mustn t say "Oh—we are God's chosen people; we are all right." Believe me, God can make anybody his "chosen people"—even these rocks here. He's like a farmer with his axe. He's already put it at the root of the trees; and he will chop down every fruitless tree for the winter fires.'

'What must we do?' people asked him.

'The man with two coats,' said John, 'must share them with the man who has none. The man with food must share it with those who are hungry.'

'Sir, what must we do?' asked the tax collectors who came to be baptized in Jordan River.

'Collect the tax,' said John, 'and nothing more than the tax.'

'What must fellows like us do?' asked some soldiers.

'No beating up people for their money,' said John, 'and no telling lies about people. Live on your soldiers' pay.'

There was great excitement in all the towns and villages.

'Is John God's Chosen Leader?' people were asking.

'I have used water as a sign that your hearts shall be made clean,' said John. 'A Stronger One than I is coming; I am not good enough to bend down and untie his shoelaces. He will really give you God's power. He'll be like fire. He'll be like a farmer at harvest when, shovel in hand, he's cleaning out his threshing floor—storing the wheat in the barn and making a bonfire of the straw.'

This was what John told the people, day in, day out.

He was not even afraid of King Herod himself. He told him that he had done wrong to marry Queen Herodias—she was not his wife but his brother's wife. He charged him with doing many other wicked things. So King Herod did a still more wicked thing—he had John thrown into prison.

Crowds came to John to be baptized in the water of Jordan River. And among them came Jesus.

He had been baptized and he was standing on the bank of the river, praying.

Then it happened. From the open heavens, God's Spirit came down on him, like a dove.

'You are my only Son,' said a voice from heaven. 'With you I am very well pleased.'

Which Way?

Jesus went away from Jordan River, his heart filled with God's Spirit. And God led him out on to the lonely moorlands.

He was there many a long day. He was being tested; he had to think things out; what did God want him to do? All this time he had nothing to eat, and at the end he was very hungry indeed.

This conversation took place in his mind: Jesus imagined himself to be sometimes on the moorlands themselves, sometimes on the top of a very high mountain, sometimes standing on top of the Temple Gate in Jerusalem.

On the moorlands:

Voice: If you are God's Son, tell this stone here to become a loaf of bread.

Jesus: The Bible says: Bread is not the only thing a man needs to live on.

On the top of a very high mountain, where he could see so far that all the world seemed to lie at his feet:

Voice: I will give you all the power of these great countries and their royal splendour. It is all mine—mine to give to anybody I want to. It can all be yours—on one condition: you must take me for your King—not God.

Jesus: The Bible says: God himself must be your King; you must be his servant and his servant only.

Jerusalem, on the top of the Temple Gate, looking down on all the people gathered in the Court below:

Voice: If you are God's Son, jump down from this high place. The Bible says: God will command his angels to look after you. And again the Bible says: Their hands will hold you fast— you won't even stub your toe on a stone.

Jesus: The Bible also says: You must not put God to the test.

The testing time of Jesus was over—but it was not the last test he had to face.

Dangers Ahead

Jesus knew that his work would be dangerous work. We know, from Mark's story, how, at the end, Jesus would meet a lonely death on a cross. But the danger was there all the time.

For Jesus came to change the way we live, and we do not like changing our way of life. He came to call us to live in God's Way; and that calls for courage and unselfishness. We must be ready for anything, and, if we meet opposition and danger. we must not give in. Jesus knew what it was to live dangerously.

So Dr. Luke now goes on to tell us what happened at the village where Jesus had grown up and where everybody knew him. We have also put here two other stories about the dangers Jesus faced.

His Own Village is Unfriendly

Jesus went back to Galilee, made strong by God's Spirit in his heart.

Everybody everywhere was talking about him. He told the people the Good News in their Meeting Houses, and everybody had a good word to say for him.

He came at last to Nazareth where he had grown up.

On the Saturday, the Holy Day of the Jews, he went along to the Meeting House there, and the leader of the Meeting House asked him to read the Bible to the people. The reading was from the book of Isaiah, one of God's great men of old. He stood up, opened the book and found these words—

> God's Spirit is in my heart;
> he has called me to my great work.
> This is what I have to do—
> give the Good News to the poor;
> tell prisoners that they are prisoners no longer,
> and blind people that they can see;
> set conquered people free,
> and tell everybody God's Great Day has come.

Jesus closed the book, gave it back to the leader of the Meeting House and sat down. Everybody was staring at him.

'You have been listening to the words of the Bible,' said Jesus. 'Today what God said would happen has happened.'

Everybody spoke well of him; they were astonished and charmed by the way he talked.

'Isn't he Joseph's son?' they were asking one another.

'I know what you will say to me—"Doctor, cure yourself",' said Jesus. ' "We've heard all about what you did down at Capernaum. Do it here in your own village." '

'No Man of God is liked by his own home-folk,' Jesus went on.

> 'There were many widows in our own country
> when Elijah was living.
> No rain fell for three long years and more,
> people starved in town and village;
> yet God sent him to none of our own countrymen,
> but only (says the Bible) "to a widow in a foreign city".
> 'There were lepers in our own country
> when Elisha was living. Yet God made none of our
> own countrymen better, only a foreign soldier.'

The people in the Meeting House were very angry when they heard him talk like this. They got up and took him outside the village to the edge of the cliff to throw him over it.

But Jesus walked through the village crowd and went on his way.

The Government is Unfriendly

One day, in Galilee, some Jewish Leaders came to Jesus.

'You'd better get out of here,' they said. 'King Herod's after you.'

'This is what I've got to say to that "fox", and you can tell him,' said Jesus. 'I shall go on doing what I have been doing, healing people who are sick in mind or body—today and tomorrow and the day after. I shall finish the work God has given me to do. A man of God is in no danger—outside Jerusalem City.'

A Foreign Village is Unfriendly

This happened in Samaria. Jesus was on his way south to Jerusalem City.

He sent friends on ahead to find somewhere to spend the night. They came to a village, but the villagers turned them out, for one reason only—Jesus and his friends, it was obvious, were on their way to Jerusalem, the Holy City of their hated enemies.

'Sir,' said James and John, when they heard this, 'you remember what happened when Elijah was turned away from a village—fire came down from the sky and burned the villagers up. Do you want us to ask God to burn these villagers up?'

Jesus turned round and stopped such talk; and they went on to another village.

Jesus himself could tell the Good News to only a few people, and they were his own countrymen. Time was short, and this was the work he believed God had given him to do.

But the Good News was for the whole world. So he gathered friends round him to learn to live in God's Way and to help him. After his death it would be *their* work to take the Good News 'to the ends of the earth'.

This is what happened. When Dr. Luke was writing his book, there were friends of Jesus in many great cities of the Roman Empire. He wanted His Excellency Theophilus to see that this was what Jesus had planned from the beginning.

In the second part of his book, Dr. Luke is going to tell how the friends of Jesus learned to follow him and carry on his work; here he tells us how they helped him in Galilee and Judea.

Peter

Jesus was one day standing right on the edge of Galilee Lake; the crowd of people, listening to the Good News about God, was pressing round him and pushing him into the water.

He noticed two boats lying just off-shore—the fishermen had landed and were washing their nets. He climbed into one of the boats—it was Peter's—and asked him to anchor it a little way out. He sat down and talked to the crowd from the boat.

At last he finished talking to them.

'Take the boat into deep water,' he said to Peter. 'Out with your nets and let's catch some fish.'

'Sir,' said Peter, 'we were out all night, hard at it, and we didn't catch one fish. But I'll get the nets out, of course, if you want me to.'

They got out the nets—and made a tremendous catch. The nets began to break, and they had to signal to their friends in the

---

Right: Galilee Lake, near Magdala, looking south.

24

other boats to come and give them a hand. Over they came, and together they filled the two boats with so many fish that they were dangerously overloaded.

When Peter saw what had happened, he fell down in front of Jesus.

'Leave me alone,' he said, 'I'm not good enough to be a friend of yours.'

He was amazed at the catch of fish, and so were James and John his fishing partners and all the men in the boat with him.

'Don't be afraid,' said Jesus to Peter. 'From now on, you will be fishing for men instead of for fish.'

They beached their boats, gave up their fishing and went along with Jesus as his comrades and friends.

The 'Twelve'

This happened in Galilee.

One day Jesus went out to 'The Hill' to pray. He spent all night thinking things out in prayer.

At daybreak he called his friends to him, and from them he chose the 'Twelve', and gave them the name 'Messengers' as well. Here is the list of the 'Twelve':

Simon   'Rock' (we say 'Peter')
Andrew, Simon's brother
James and John
Philip
Bartholomew
Matthew
Thomas
James, the son of Alphaeus
Simon   'Rebel'
Judas, the son of James
Judas (who later handed Jesus over to the Jewish Leaders).

One day Jesus gave some special work to seventy-two of his friends. He was going through Galilee, telling people the Good News about God. He wanted them as his 'advance party'—to go ahead of him, two together, to any town or village he was going to visit.

This is what Jesus told them.

'There's a wonderful harvest; but there aren't enough harvesters. God is the owner of the harvest fields. Ask him to send harvesters out into the fields.

'Go; remember it's dangerous work; I am sending you like lambs to a pack of wolves.

'Here are your orders: no money-bag, no knapsack, no sandals, no greetings on the road.

'The first words you must say when you enter a house are— "Peace to this house". If a man who cares for peace lives there, your greeting will do his heart good. If he's not that sort of man, your greeting will at least do your own heart good.

'Make one house your home, and share meals with the people who live there—a workman should be paid. But don't go changing homes.

'If you come to a town and the townspeople are friendly, eat whatever they give you. Heal the sick people there and tell them— "God himself, in all his power, is here among you".

'If you come to a town, and the townspeople are unfriendly, go out into the streets. Tell them—"The dust of your town is sticking to our feet; we wipe it off to show you what sort of people you are. Yet your unfriendliness makes no difference to this: God himself, in all his power, is here among you". Believe me, the old foreign city of Sodom, wicked as it was, will do better than that town in God's Great Day.'[1]

---

[1] Look up the poem of Jesus, 'Six Cities', *The Message*, p. 75.

Martha and Mary

One day, on his travels, Jesus came to a village. A woman called Martha welcomed him into her home. She had a sister called Mary.

Mary used to sit beside Jesus, listening to him talking; Martha went hurrying about the house, doing this and that and the other.

Suddenly, she stopped in front of Jesus.

'Sir,' she said, 'doesn't it matter to you that my sister leaves me to do all the housework by myself? Tell her to give me a hand.'

'Martha, Martha,' said Jesus, 'what a lot of things you worry and fuss about! There's only one thing that matters. Mary's choice is better; nobody can ever take it away from her.'

Women who helped

Jesus and the 'Twelve' were going about the countryside, visiting towns and villages, telling the people the Good News about God.

Some women went along with them too—women who had been ill and whom Jesus had cured. One of them was Mary from the village of Magdala—she had been very ill indeed. Another was Joanna; she was the wife of one of the great officers of the court of King Herod. Another was Susanna. There were many others too. They used their own money to look after Jesus and his friends.

THE PURPOSE OF THE VENTURE: BREAKING DOWN ALL BARRIERS

Jesus believed that God's will is that the world should be his Family and live in his Way.

Men and women were not living together as a Family. They were divided from one another by all sorts of barriers. There were barriers between rich and poor. People hated other people, as the Jewish people of his day hated the Roman soldiers. There were barriers, too, between individual people.

We must learn, Jesus believed, to break all these barriers down if we are to live in God's Way. There will always be differences between people; but we must not let them become barriers separating us from one another. We must use our differences to make our lives richer and wider.

Dr. Luke was amazed at the way Jesus cared for people, especially for those whom nobody else cared for. He has told us many stories about the way Jesus took no notice of what people thought about him, but treated everybody he met, even if they were lepers or outcasts, as persons and equals.

A Roman Officer

Jesus was in Capernaum; a detachment of Roman soldiers was stationed there.

One of the captain's slaves, a man of whom he was very fond, was dangerously ill. The captain heard that Jesus was in town, and he sent a message to him by some Jewish Leaders, who were friends of his, to ask him to come and cure his slave.

They found Jesus; they were very keen to get him to help the captain.

'He deserves help like this,' they said. 'He's a friend of all Jewish people. It was he who built our Meeting House for us.'

Jesus went along with them.

He had almost reached the house, when the captain again sent some of his friends to meet him.

'Sir,' he sent word, 'don't go to any more trouble. It wouldn't be fitting for you to come inside my house; that's why I didn't think it was right for me to come to meet you myself. Give the word of command, and my boy will be well. I am an officer in the army; there are generals over me and soldiers under me, and I know what orders are. I tell this soldier to go, and he goes; I tell that soldier to come, and he comes; I tell my slave to do this, and he does it.'

Jesus was filled with admiration for this Roman captain.

He turned to the crowd.

The Gravestone of a Roman soldier who died on active service in Palestine: 'In memory of L. Magnius Felix, a soldier of the Tenth Legion, the Fretensis, orderly to the Colonel, 18 years in the army, 39 years of age'.

'Believe me,' he said, 'I haven't found a Jew who trusted me like this.'

The captain's friends went back to the house, and they found the slave fit and well.

A Widow

On another day Jesus came to the village of Nain. His friends and a lot of other people were walking along the road with him.

At the town gate, there was a large crowd of people coming out. It was the funeral of the only son of a widow.

Jesus saw her and felt very sorry for her.

'Don't cry,' he said to her.

He went up to the coffin and touched it; the bearers stood still.

'Young man,' he said, 'get up.'

The dead man sat up and spoke.

Like Elijah in the old Bible story, Jesus gave him back to his mother.

Everybody felt that God himself was with them.

'Praise be to God!' they said.

'A great man has come among us!'

'God cares for his people.'

News of this spread throughout the whole of Palestine and beyond its borders.

A Woman who was 'a Bad Lot'

One day a Jewish Leader, Simon by name, asked Jesus out to dinner. So they went along together to his home and sat down to dinner.

Now there was a woman in the town who, in the eyes of religious people, was 'a bad lot'; the people who went to the Meeting House wouldn't have anything to do with her. She heard that Jesus was having dinner in Simon's house, and this is what she did. She got hold of a bottle of real Indian ointment. She went and stood behind the couch on which Jesus was reclining. She was crying, and her tears fell on his feet. She wiped them dry with her hair, kissing them and putting ointment on them again and again.

Simon noticed all this.

'If this man was really a Man of God,' he thought, 'he'd know who was touching him like this, and what kind of woman she was. He'd know she was "a bad lot".'

Jesus was in no doubt about what Simon was thinking.

'Simon,' he said. 'I've something to say to you.'

'Go ahead,' said Simon.

Jesus turned to the woman.

'You see this woman,' he said. 'I came home with you, but you didn't give me any water to wash my feet; this woman wet my feet with her tears and dried them with her hair. You didn't greet me with a kiss; this woman has kissed my feet again and again ever since she came in. You didn't give me any perfume to put on my head; she's put ointment on my feet.

'Listen: because of her great love, all the wrong things she's done—and they are many—are forgiven. You don't show much love for me, do you? But then, you don't feel you need to be forgiven.'

Jesus turned to the woman.

'All the wrong things you've done are already forgiven,' he said.

The guests started whispering to one another.

'Who's this? He's even forgiving people's sins!'

'It's your trust in me that's saved you,' said Jesus to the woman. 'Go home and don't worry.'

Lepers

Jesus was on his way to Jerusalem. He was passing through the border country of Samaria and Galilee, and he went into one of the villages. On the road into the village, ten men met him—all lepers. But they kept their distance.

'Jesus! Sir!' they shouted to him. 'Take pity on us!'

Jesus saw them.

'You know the law for lepers who are cured,' he called back. 'Go and show yourself to the priest.'

Right: EXODUS. Sara Cohen, aged 11, painted this picture. She lives in Israel, the same country in which Gideon and David and Jeremiah lived and which was the native land of Jesus. She has painted a story which Jesus heard when he was a boy.

Off the lepers went; and as they walked along the road they found they were lepers no longer—they were cured.

One of the men turned back to say 'Thank you'.

'Praise be to God!' he kept shouting loudly. He fell down on his face at the feet of Jesus and thanked him. He was the only one who wasn't a Jew; he was a 'foreigner' from Samaria.

'There were ten lepers cured, weren't there?' asked Jesus. 'What's happened to the other nine? Was this "foreigner" the only one who could come back and say "Thank you" to God?'

'Get up and go home,' he said to him. 'It's your trust in me that's made you well.'

A Chief Tax Collector

One day Jesus was going through Jericho City.

Now there lived in Jericho a very rich man called Zacchaeus, manager of the Tax Office there. He was very keen to see what sort of person Jesus was; but he was a little man and he couldn't see over the heads of the crowds. So he ran on ahead along the road Jesus was taking; and to get a good view of him he climbed into a fig tree.

Jesus came along the road and looked up at Zacchaeus in the tree.

'Zacchaeus,' he said, 'you'd better be quick and get down— I must stay with you today.'

He was down in a moment, thrilled to have Jesus as his guest.

The crowd didn't like it.

'He's staying with that scoundrel of a fellow,' they muttered. Zacchaeus stopped.

Left : A RABBI. Nili, who is 12 and painted this picture, lives in Israel as Sara Cohen does. There are Rabbis (religious teachers) in Israel today as there were when Jesus lived in Galilee.

'I'm not the man they think I am, Sir,' he said to Jesus. 'Look, I give half my income to people in need; and if I've taken more than I ought from anybody, I give four times as much back.'

'God himself has come to this home today,' said Jesus. 'This man belongs to God's family too. You know what God said in the Bible—"I will seek the lost". That's what I and my friends are doing.'

THE COST OF THE VENTURE

Dr. Luke has already told us about the dangers Jesus faced. Now he faces the greatest danger of all.

Jesus has told the Good News in Galilee. He must also tell the Good News in the capital city of his country. At the Great Feast, Jewish pilgrims from all over the world would be in Jerusalem City. Jesus would have the chance of speaking to as many of his countrymen as possible.

What drove Jesus forward was his love for people. He loved them because God his Father loved them. He knew the danger he would face in Jerusalem. His going to Jerusalem shows how great his love was, and what it cost him.

Reaching the City

Jesus had climbed the mountain road from Jericho and had almost reached Jerusalem City. He had come to the spot where the road begins to drop down from the top of the Olive Hill into the valley. Crowds of pilgrims were going along the road. All his friends were very happy and were singing hymns of praise to God for all they had seen Jesus do. The words came from an old Jewish hymn—

> Praise to the King
>   who comes in God's name!
> Peace in heaven!
>   Glory in heaven!

There were some Jewish Leaders among the crowd.

'Sir,' they said, 'tell your friends to stop singing.'

'Believe me,' said Jesus, 'if my friends were to stop singing, the rocks would shout out!'

As Jesus went on down the road, he saw Jerusalem City across the valley. His eyes filled with tears.

'If only today you knew how to live for peace instead of war! [he said]
>   You cannot see what you are doing.
>   The time will come when
>   your enemies will throw up a pallisade round you,
>   besiege and attack you on all sides,
>   dash down your buildings and your people,
>   leave not a wall upstanding:
>   all because you did not see that God had already come to
>   you in love, not war.'

Every day Jesus went into the Temple to tell the people the Good News about God. The Jewish Leaders had made up their minds to get rid of him, but they couldn't do anything about it. The crowds listened to him, spell-bound.

The Supper

It was near the time for The Great Feast to begin, when all Jews remember together how God rescued them from Egypt and sent Moses to lead them to their homeland.

Jesus and his friends sat down at supper together.

'I have looked forward eagerly to sharing this Great Feast with you before I die,' he said. 'I shall never share it with you again until all it means has come true and God's Great Day has come.'

He took the cup in his hands and said Grace.

'Take this cup,' he said, 'and share it among yourselves. Believe me, I shall drink no more wine like this until God's Great Day comes.'

His friends started quarrelling about who was the most important person among them.

'Foreign kings,' said Jesus to them, 'are dictators to the people of their country; and powerful governors are called "Father and Friend" of their people. You—my friends—must turn it all the other way round. The "most important person" among you must live just as if he was the youngest among you. The "Leader" of my friends must live as the servant of all the others. Who is "the most important person"—the man who's having supper or the waiter who's looking after him? I know what you'll say—the man who's having supper, of course. Yet I have lived among you like the waiter who looks after the needs of other people.

'You are the ones who have stood by me, all through the hard times I have had,' Jesus went on. 'I will give you real "royalty"—the kind of "royalty" my Father has given me; you will have supper with me, as we are having supper together tonight, at *my* "Royal Court" and you'll be the real "Leaders" of God's People.'

Jesus turned to Simon Peter.

'Simon, Simon,' he said, 'Satan's after you to see the kind of man you are—like a farmer shaking and sifting wheat at harvest. But I have asked my Father that your trust in me may not break down. When you've won through, stand by my other friends—your brothers in God's Family.'

'Sir,' said Peter, 'I'd face prison and death with you—now.'

'When I sent you out to tell people the Good News about God,' said Jesus, 'you went without purse or bag or sandals. Did you find you were ever in real need?'

'No,' they said.

'Now it's very different,' said Jesus. 'You'll need everything you've got—purse and bag and sword; if you haven't a sword,

Right : JERUSALEM CITY—the Damascus Gate.

36

you'd better sell your coat and buy one! You remember what the Bible says—"God's Servant was treated like a criminal"?—that's what I've got to face. It will all happen as the Bible has made clear.'

'Sir,' they said, 'see—here are two swords.'

'Enough of this,' said Jesus.

In the Orchard

Jesus set off for the Olive Hill—a spot he was very fond of—and his friends went along with him.

'The real test is coming,' said Jesus when they got there. 'You'd better pray that you won't have to face it.'

He went off a little way by himself.

He knelt down on the ground.

'Father,' he prayed. 'Take this suffering away from me. Yet I will do what you want, not what I want.'

God gave him the strength he needed. He was in very great distress, and he prayed with all his heart. Sweat fell from him on to the ground like drops of blood.

He finished praying and stood up. He went over to his friends and found them asleep, tired out by sadness.

'Why are you sleeping like this?' he said to them. 'Get up and pray that you won't have to face the real test that's coming!'

Before he had finished speaking a crowd of men rushed on them; and there, at their head, was the man called Judas, one of his close friends. He went right up to Jesus to greet him with a kiss, as if he was just meeting him.

'Judas,' said Jesus, 'is it with a kiss that you are handing me and my friends over to these men?'

His friends saw what was going to happen.

'Sir,' they said, 'shall we draw our swords?'

One of them hit out with his sword at one of the Temple police.

'Stop!' said Jesus. 'Let them have their way.'

He touched the man's ear and healed him.

'This is your hour indeed, the night and all its darkness,' said Jesus to the officers of the Temple guard.

The men arrested Jesus and marched him off to the High Court.

The soldiers guarding Jesus made fun of him and beat him up. They covered his face with a cloth.

'Be a real Man of God now,' they said, 'and tell us who struck you!'

And they swore at him again and again.

Jesus on Trial

When it was daybreak, the Jewish Leaders had Jesus brought before their Council.

'Are you God's Chosen Leader?' they said. 'Tell us.'

'You won't believe me if I tell you,' said Jesus. 'You won't answer any questions I ask you. Do you remember the dream Daniel saw at night?—

> In the cloudy heavens
>   I saw the figure of a man
> coming into God's presence
>   and being presented to him.

> God gave him power and honour
>   and made him king.
> His power shall last
>   for ever;
> his kingly rule
>   shall never be overthrown.

'This will all come true—from this very moment.'

'You are God's Son then?' they all called out.

'It's you who use the words,' said Jesus.

'What are we bothering about evidence for?' they said. 'We've heard it for ourselves from his own lips!'

The whole Council got up and took him to Pilate, the Roman Governor.

These were the charges brought against him.

'This fellow calls himself a king,' they said. 'We've found him raising rebellion and telling citizens not to pay their taxes to the Emperor.'

'Are you the Jewish King?' Pilate asked Jesus.

'It's you who use the word,' he said.

'My judgment,' Pilate told the Jewish Leaders and the crowds, 'is that the man's innocent.'

They wouldn't have that.

'He's a mob leader,' they said. 'All over the south he's spreading his ideas. He started in the north, in Galilee, and now he's here in the capital city!'

'Is the fellow a Galilean?' Pilate asked, when he heard the word 'Galilee'.

When he found out that Jesus belonged to the country Herod ruled, Pilate sent Jesus off to him for trial, for he was in the city for the Feast.

Herod was very glad to see Jesus. He had heard many stories about him, and for a very long time had wanted to see him—he wanted to see him do a miracle. He asked him all sorts of questions, but Jesus made no reply.

The Jewish Leaders were standing near Jesus, loudly telling Herod all the crimes they said he was guilty of. Herod and his soldiers insulted him and made fun of him. At last, Herod dressed him like a real king and sent him back to Pilate.

Pilate and Herod had been enemies, but on this day they became good friends.

Pilate sent for the Jewish Leaders.

'You brought this man before me as a mob-leader,' he said. 'You were here when I examined him. I found nothing in what you had to say against him. Nor did Herod—he just sent him back to this court. He hasn't done anything that deserves the death sentence. I'll flog him and set him free.'

'Take him away!' the crowd shouted all together. 'Set Barabbas free for us!' (Barabbas had been thrown into prison as a murderer and a leader of a rebellion in the city.)

Pilate wanted to set Jesus free; so he called out to the crowd again. But they kept on shouting—

'Hang him on a cross! Hang him on a cross!'

Pilate spoke a third time to the crowd.

'But what's he done wrong? I find him innocent of anything that deserves the death sentence. I'll flog him and set him free.'

The crowd went on yelling, demanding the death sentence. The shouting of the crowd won the day, and Pilate gave orders that they should have their way.

He set free the man who had been imprisoned for rebellion and murder—the man they were asking for; and he handed Jesus over to them—they could do what they liked with him.

At Skull Hill

Jesus was not alone when he died; two other men, both bandits, were marched off with him to be put to death on Skull Hill. They hung all three on crosses; Jesus hung between the other two.

'Father,' Jesus kept on praying, 'forgive them. They don't know what they are doing.'

The soldiers went on tossing up for his clothes and then shared them out. The crowds stood by, watching.

The Jewish Leaders just laughed at him.

'He could save other people all right!' they sneered. 'Let him save himself now—if he really is God's Chosen Leader!'

The soldiers also joined in the foolery. They marched up to him and presented him with their sour wine.

'Get yourself out of this—if you are the Jewish King!' they called out.

Above the head of Jesus was the notice: THE JEWISH KING.

One of the bandits hanging alongside him cursed him too.

'You're God's Chosen Leader, are you?' he shouted. 'Get yourself and us out of this, then!'

The other bandit told him to be quiet.

'Aren't you afraid even of God?' he said. 'You've been given the same sentence as he has. We deserve it; we're guilty. This man hasn't done anything wrong.'

He turned to Jesus.

'Don't forget me,' he said, 'when you are King.'

'Believe me,' said Jesus, 'you'll be with me in heaven itself—today.'

Then Jesus raised his voice.

'Father,' he prayed (in the words of an old hymn), 'I put my whole life in your hands.'

With these words he died.

The officer in charge of the guard was watching.

'This man was innocent,' he said.

The crowds who had come out to see the three men die were staring at everything that happened. They went home, horrified at what they had seen.

The friends of Jesus watched all this from a distance.

The women who had come with Jesus from Galilee were among them. When his body was taken down from the cross they followed, and found out where the grave was and how his body was placed in it. Then they went home to get perfumes ready.

When Jesus had been arrested and executed, his friends thought everything was over.

They had not really understood Jesus. They thought he would be the great deliverer of his people from their enemies. But he was not this sort of deliverer. Now he was dead, there was nothing more that they could do. Dr. Luke wants us to see how certain they were that the story was finished.

But it certainly was not finished. To their great surprise, they found that the story had only just begun. This is his account of what happened.

We shall not discuss this important story here. But in *Paul the Explorer*, we shall see what this story meant to Paul, and, in *Jesus Leader and Lord*, what he and John, who wrote the Fourth Gospel, had to say about it.

The Women at the Grave

The women rested on the Saturday—work of all kinds on the Holy Day was forbidden by Jewish law.

At dawn, on Sunday morning, they went to the grave and took the perfumes that they had got ready. They found that someone had already rolled away the great stone from the mouth of the cave. They went inside but found it empty.

They didn't know what to do. Suddenly two men in shining clothes came right up to them. The women were very frightened— they didn't dare even to look up at them.

'Why are you looking for someone who is alive—in a graveyard where there are only dead people?' the men asked. 'Remember what he told you when he was still in Galilee—that he must be handed over to men who didn't live in God's way and face death itself, but that his death would not be the end.'

Then they remembered that Jesus had told them this. They left the grave and went back to report everything that had happened to the eleven close friends of Jesus and all the others. But their story seemed to the others a lot of nonsense; nobody believed a word of it.

On a Country Road

That same Sunday two friends of Jesus—one of them was Cleopas—were walking back to a village, the village of Emmaus, about seven miles away. They were discussing what had happened on the Friday.

As they talked and argued, Jesus himself joined them and walked along the road with them. They looked at him, but he didn't seem to be anybody they knew.

'What's all the talk about?' he asked.

They stopped, looking completely downcast.

'Are you the only visitor in the city who doesn't know what's been going on this last day or two?' said Cleopas.

'What?' he asked.

'Why,' they said, 'all this about Jesus from Nazareth. He was a Man of God indeed—you could tell that from the way he talked and what he did. He made God real—and everybody knew it. Our Leaders handed him over to the Roman Government to sentence to death, and they hung him on a cross. He'd made us all feel that he was the man to set our people free; but he wasn't.

'The story's three days old now,' they added. 'Some of our own women, though, gave us a shock this morning. They were at his grave at dawn; but it was empty, they said, and they came back with a story, if you please, about seeing angels—angels who talked about his being alive. Some of us went off to the grave there and then. The women's story about the body was true all right, but they didn't see anything of Jesus himself.'

'How dull you are!' said Jesus. 'How slow you are to see what the Bible's all about! Hadn't God's Chosen Leader got to face death like this? Wasn't this his only way to triumph?'

He told them the whole Bible story again. He began with Moses who led the people out of Egypt and went on to talk about the great Men of God like Isaiah and Jeremiah. He showed them what *they* had to say about God's Chosen Leader.

By this time they had reached the village and the end of their

journey. Jesus was going on along the road beyond the village, and they had some trouble in persuading him to stop there.

'Come in and stay with us,' they said. 'It's getting dark and daylight will soon be gone.'

So he went home with them.

It was supper time, and he sat down at the table with them.

He picked up a loaf, said Grace, broke it and gave it to them to eat. They were looking at him, and suddenly they knew who he was—and he was gone!

'Wasn't it thrilling to listen to him as we walked along the road,' they said to one another, 'and didn't he make the Bible come alive?'

They got up at once and were off back to the city. They found the eleven close friends and other friends in the room together.

'He's really alive again,' the men in the room told them. 'Peter's seen him!'

The two of them reported what had happened as they were walking along the road, and how they'd realized who he was when he broke the loaf at supper.

In the House

The friends of Jesus went on talking together. Suddenly Jesus himself stood there in the room with them. They were scared and terrified; they thought they were seeing a ghost.

'What are you troubled about?' asked Jesus. 'Why are you so full of doubts? Look at my hands and my feet—it's me. Touch me and look at me—you can't touch a ghost as you can touch me.'

They couldn't believe what they saw, for joy and astonishment.

'Have you anything to eat?' he asked.

They gave him a piece of cooked fish, and they watched him take it and eat it.

He went on to make the story of the Bible plain to them so that they could see what it was really about.

'I told you all this when we were in Galilee together,' he said. 'What the Bible says about the work I've been doing must come true. You know what it says—God's Chosen Leader must face death, but his death isn't the end of everything; he will soon rise to life again. This must be told to everybody everywhere, all over the world, starting from this city. People must be told that if they change their ways God will forgive them for all the wrong things they have done. You know this is true—you have seen it all with your own eyes.

'Look, I shall give you what God my Father promised—his own power in your hearts. But you must stay here in this city until you are given it.'

At Bethany

Jesus took his friends out of the city, almost as far as Bethany Village.

He lifted his hands up in prayer and asked God to be with them. And while he was praying he left them.

They went back to the city as happy as could be; they almost lived in the Temple, thanking God for all he had done.

46

Part Two—Across the World

In the first part of my work, Your Excellency, I have told the story of Jesus—all he began to do and say. I bring this to an end by telling you what orders he gave to his friends on the day when he was taken up from us.

After his death, for a month or more, he showed himself alive again to his friends and talked to them about God's Way. While he was with them, he told them not to leave the city.

'You must wait here,' he said, 'until God gives you his power, as he has promised to do and as I have told you. John the Hermit baptized people with water; before long God will give you his own power in your hearts.'

The second part of my work tells you what happened then.

Luke

The story now begins again. Jesus is alive again! That makes all the difference.

God's raising Jesus to life again is the part of the story that many people find very difficult to believe. 'We can believe', they say, 'that Jesus was a good and great man; but how can we believe that such an improbable and amazing thing as this happened?'

We shall come back to this in our last book, *Jesus Leader and Lord*, where we shall see what Paul and John had to say about it. For they found it just as improbable and amazing as we do; and yet they were sure it happened.

The first Friends[1] of Jesus did not agree among themselves just how it happened. After all, they never expected it to happen and they were taken by surprise; they had thought, when they saw Jesus executed, that it was all over and finished. (Look up 'On a Country Road', p. 44.)

But now they knew that the death of Jesus was by no means the end of the story. They gave as honest an account as they could of what happened; they knew that Jesus was their Friend for ever, and now they were ready to die for him, if need be. Four of them—and these were not all—did die for him: Stephen, James (John's brother), Peter and Paul. Knowing that Jesus was alive for ever made them new men and gave them their courage.

The World Adventure had now clearly begun. Four men took a leading part in it.

Stephen was the first to see that Palestine was too small for Jesus; only the world itself was big enough, for God's love is for everybody. He was the first man to die for Jesus.

---

[1] We shall print 'Friends of Jesus' with a capital letter in this part. This was one of the names Christians used for themselves in the earliest days (look up Acts 27. 3, John 14. 14–15).

Right: ANTIOCH IN SYRIA. In the time of Jesus this was the third largest city in the world. Its streets were brilliantly lit at night, and many rich people came to live there. It was in this city that the friends of Jesus made 'The Great Plan' to take the Good News to the whole world.

Philip went to Samaria; he was also the first man to win an Egyptian as a Friend of Jesus.

Peter and Paul were the great leaders.

Dr. Luke tells us, in a very vivid story, how Peter came to see that 'God has no favourites'. He welcomed a Roman officer as a Friend of Jesus, and told the Friends of Jesus in Jerusalem City that they must be much bolder than they had been.

But Paul was the man who saw clearly what Jesus wanted his Friends to do—the man who, when the story begins, was his bitter enemy. He knew that the Good News must be told to Jew and foreigner alike. We shall tell Paul's story in *Paul the Explorer*. Here we have chosen six stories from Dr. Luke's notebook to show how the Good News was taken to Cyprus, Anatolia, Asia and Greece until at last it reached Rome itself. Dr. Luke must have been very proud that it was the Friends of Jesus in his own city of Antioch who took the lead in this world adventure.

We do not know who first told the Good News in Rome; there were Friends of Jesus in the city and in other Italian towns, as you will see, when Paul got there. Perhaps Italian Jewish merchants heard the Good News when they were pilgrims in Jerusalem, and took it home with them. When Dr. Luke tells us how Paul came as a prisoner to Rome, he wants us to see him as the representative of all the Friends of Jesus who took the Good News 'to the ends of the earth'.

Left: 'THE MOST FAMOUS CITY IN THE WORLD'. The city of Athens was the greatest of the Greek cities. It had played a great part in the history of the Greek people, and famous people had lived there. Pillars of the temple on the Acropolis are still standing.

You will notice, as the story begins again, how far the Friends of Jesus were from understanding him. They still thought he was going to be the deliverer of his people from their enemies.

So, at the beginning of the second part of the story, Dr. Luke tells us what orders Jesus gave his Friends. They were to tell the Good News in Jerusalem City, but they were not to stop there. They were to go out all over the world.

They would need God's own power to do God's work. So Dr. Luke goes on to tell us how, a few weeks later, God's power was given to them.

The Last Words of Jesus

Jesus and his Friends were together on the hill called 'Olive Orchard'.

'Lord,' they asked him, 'will you now make the Jewish people a free nation again?'

'That's God's business!' said Jesus. 'It's not your business to ask "How long are we going to be an occupied country?" or "When shall we be free?" You will be given God's own power when his spirit comes into your hearts; and then *your* business will be to go all over the world to tell everybody what you know about me. You must start here in this city first of all, go out into your own homeland, and then right to the very ends of the earth.'

With these words, Jesus was hidden by a cloud and they saw him no more.

His Friends went back to the city and to the room where they were staying. They were all there—Peter, John, James, Andrew, Philip, Thomas, Bartholomew, Matthew, James (whose father was Alphaeus), Simon (who had been a member of the Resistance Movement) and Judas (the one whose father was James). They spent their time together in prayer. The women Friends of Jesus were there too—and his mother, Mary, and his brothers.

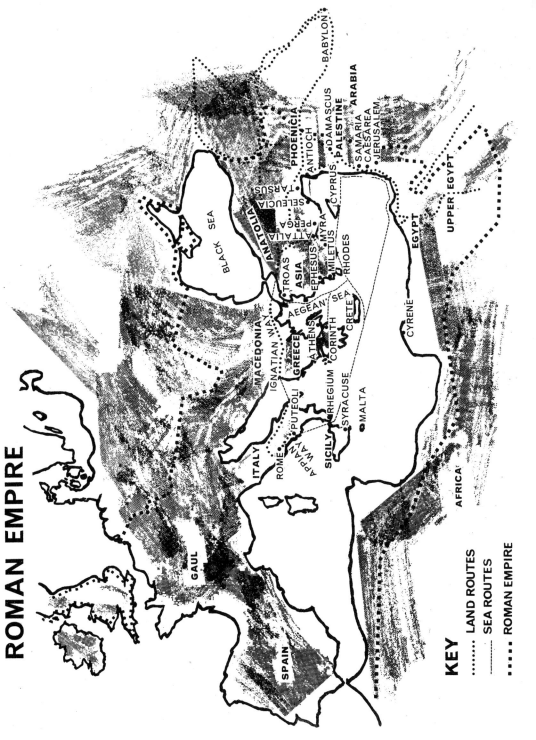

ROMAN EMPIRE

KEY

...... LAND ROUTES

—— SEA ROUTES

▪▪▪▪ ROMAN EMPIRE

SPAIN

GAUL

ITALY

ROME

APPIAN WAY

PUTEOLI

RHEGIUM

SICILY

SYRACUSE

MALTA

AFRICA

CYRENE

EGYPT

UPPER EGYPT

MACEDONIA

IGNATIAN WAY

GREECE

ATHENS

CORINTH

AEGEAN SEA

CRETE

BLACK SEA

ANATOLIA

TROAS

ASIA

EPHESUS

MILETUS

RHODES

PERGA

ATTALIA

MYRA

SELEUCIA

TARSUS

CYPRUS

ANTIOCH

PHOENICIA

DAMASCUS

PALESTINE

ARABIA

SAMARIA

CAESAREA

JERUSALEM

BABYLON

It was now the time of the Feast, 'The Fiftieth Day' (Pentecost), when Jewish people remembered how Moses gave them God's Law on Mount Sinai.

The Friends of Jesus were all together in the house where they were staying. Then it happened. Suddenly—as if a storm of wind and fire burst upon them—they were all filled with God's own power and they began to talk in many strange ways. God gave them the power to speak out boldly.

Jewish pilgrims from lands all over the world were staying in Jerusalem City; they came from Mesopotamia in the east, from the shores of the Black Sea in the north, from Egypt in the south, and even from Rome in the west.

A great crowd gathered, talking excitedly; they were amazed and didn't know what to think.

'What's all this about?' they were asking.

Others thought it was all very queer.

'They're all drunk,' they said.

Peter stood up, and the other close Friends of Jesus stood up with him. He shouted over the noise of the crowd.

'Men of the South! Citizens of this city!' he called out. 'This is something you all ought to know about—so listen to me. You've got it all wrong. These men aren't drunk—after all, it's only nine o'clock in the morning. What's happened is something you'll find in your Bibles. Do you remember these words?—

> In the days that are to be
>   I will give my Spirit to everybody;
> Your people shall understand me—
>   Your old men shall dream dreams
>   Your young men shall see visions.
> Even to slaves
>   I will give my Spirit.

'My fellow countrymen, listen to me.

'You yourselves know all about Jesus of Nazareth. He lived and worked among you. All he did was proof enough that God sent him and that God was with him. He cured sick people; that was a sign of God's power. You handed him over to the Romans and killed him. This, indeed, was all part of God's plan, for God raised him to life again; death could not be the end of his work. All of us here have met him and been with him since his death and know he is alive. God has given him high honour. Long ago God promised to give us his own power in our hearts; he has kept his promise and through Jesus he has given us his power. These are not idle words; you can see and hear for yourselves. Let all the Jewish people be in no doubt that God has made the man you killed Leader and Lord.'

They were very troubled when Peter spoke like this.

'Brother men,' they said, 'what shall we do?'

'You must change your ways,' said Peter, 'join the company of the Friends of Jesus as a sign that you are really sorry, and know that God has forgiven you. God will give you the power of his Spirit in your hearts. His promise is for all the Jewish people— you and your descendants; and it's not only for Jewish people; it is, as the Bible says, "for all those who live in far-off lands", everybody everywhere. What matters is not who we are but whom God calls.'

Peter told them the story of Jesus again and again and called them to make up their minds.

'This is a dishonest world today,' he said. 'Have nothing to do with its dishonesty.'

About three thousand people accepted what Peter said, and joined the company of the Friends of Jesus.

Many of the Friends of Jesus still did not understand what he wanted them to do. They told the Good News in Jerusalem City, as he had told them to do; but it looks as if they thought that this was *all* he wanted them to do.

They were certainly changed men and women, very different people from what they had been before. They were brave, and they lived together as members of God's Family. They faced the anger of the people and of the Jewish Leaders with courage, and they told the Good News fearlessly.

But they were soon to learn how much more Jesus wanted them to do.

How the Friends of Jesus lived

The Friends of Jesus made a great stir in the city.

They lived day by day in God's Way as Jesus had shown them; Peter and James and John explained it to them.

They lived together like members of one family.

When they had supper together, they broke the loaf, shared it as Jesus had done at the last supper on the night before he died, and remembered what Jesus had done for everybody everywhere.

They spent much time in prayer.

They lived together and shared everything with one another. They sold their property and possessions and shared the money out so that nobody went without anything he needed. Every day they went to Temple worship, and met at home to 'break the loaf' together. They shared their meals together with real happiness. All this was their way of thanking God for all he had done for them. The people in the city thought well of them. Day by day, with God's help, their numbers grew.

They were one in heart and mind, and none of them thought that his own things were just for his own use—they were for everybody to share. So the close Friends of Jesus, like Peter, made it very clear what 'Jesus being alive again' really meant.

They were a happy company. Nobody went without what he needed. The rich people among them sold their lands and houses, and brought the money they got to their leaders. It was then shared out as each had need.

Here is an example. One of them, Joseph, was a rich man (Peter and his friends called him Barnabas). He was born in the island of Cyprus but he worked in the Temple, helping in the services there. He owned a field. He went and sold it and brought the money to the leaders.

More and more people, crowds of men and women, believed in Jesus and joined his company of Friends. Just as Jesus healed those who were ill, so did his Friends. People brought sick people on beds and mats out into the streets.

'Peter's shadow will fall on them as he walks along,' they said.

They brought the sick from villages outside the city, too.

Clash with the Jewish Leaders
How the Trouble began

Peter and John were walking one day up to the Temple. It was three o'clock in the afternoon, and people were gathering there for prayer.

In those days, a cripple whom everybody knew used to sit at one of the Temple gates—the 'Beautiful Gate'. He had been a cripple all his life, and his family put him there to beg from people as they were going into the Temple. This afternoon he was being carried to his pitch just as Peter and John came along. He caught sight of them and asked them for money.

They stopped.

'Look at us,' said Peter, watching him closely.

He stared back at them both; he thought he was going to get something.

'I've no money,' said Peter, 'but I'll give you what I have: In the name of Jesus of Nazareth, get up and walk.'

He got hold of the man's hand and pulled him up. His feet and ankles became strong at once; he jumped about, stood still and walked round. Then he went into the Temple with Peter and John, now walking, now jumping, and thanking God all the time.

The crowd saw him walking round and thanking God. One after another they realized who he was—he was the beggar at the Temple Gate! They were amazed at what had happened to him. He kept holding on to Peter and John, and the people came crowding round them.

By now they had got as far as Solomon's Porch; and, when Peter saw what a crowd there was, he stood and faced them.

'Fellow countrymen,' he said, 'why does this surprise you? Why do you stare at us? There's nothing special about *us*; we didn't make this man walk about like this. Remember what the Bible says—"The God of our fathers, who has cared for us from the beginning of our history . . . has given great honour to his Servant"; the words "his Servant" there mean Jesus.'

He went on to tell them again the story of Jesus, how he died and how he was alive again.

'It was his trust in Jesus,' he said, 'that has made a healthy man of this beggar you all know so well. I know that you didn't really know what you were doing when you treated Jesus as you did. But he is God's Servant, and God raised him to life for your good, to get you to change your ways.'

At this moment the chief of police and some priests pushed their way in. They didn't want the Friends of Jesus to talk to the people like this and tell them that Jesus was alive. They arrested Peter and John and took them off to prison for the night, for it was now getting dark.

The fact was that many of the people had taken Peter at his word—the number was reckoned at about five thousand.

Next morning, the Council of the Jewish Leaders were called together—the judges who had sentenced Jesus to death were among them. Peter and John were put in the dock.

'By what right did you do this?' the judges asked. 'Who are you?'

Peter spoke out—a man inspired.

'My lords,' he said, 'are we being questioned about a good deed done to a lame man? I can tell you the answer—and the whole country ought to know: in the name of Jesus of Nazareth, dead on a cross, raised by God to life again, this man stands before you in good health. We know what you think of Jesus—but do you remember the words of the Bible—

> The stone the builders would not use
> has become the key stone?

'There's no other way to put things right—only by the way Jesus made plain. One man, and one man only, matters for everybody everywhere—and that man is Jesus.'

The members of the Council stared at the boldness of Peter and John. They knew that they were laymen without any proper education, and they were amazed. And they knew, too, that they had been in the company of Jesus. But there was the beggar himself standing in the court, as healthy as any of them; how could they say nothing had happened?

They had the men taken out of court. They had to talk this matter over together.

'What are we going to do with these men?'

That was the question.

'Everybody in the city knows what these men have done.'

'We can't say it didn't happen.'

'We don't want the report to spread far and wide.'

'We'd better just let them off with a warning and tell them not to talk about Jesus any more.'

They decided just to warn them.

They called Peter and John back, and told them what the judgment of the court was: no more public speaking of any kind anywhere about Jesus of Nazareth; all this must stop.

'Well,' the two men said, 'you must make up your own minds whom we ought to obey—you or God—when we are doing God's work. Our duty is plain—we can't stop talking about what we ourselves have seen and heard.'

The Council repeated its warning and then set them free. They couldn't think of any way of punishing them. The crowds made that impossible; all over the city they were saying that God was behind it all.

'After all, the beggar was over forty years old,' the people said.

Peter and John went back to their friends, free men, and told them what the Council had said.

Prison Again

Peter and John and the other Friends of Jesus went on telling the Good News. They met together in the Temple. Many people joined their company, and many sick people were cured.

The Jewish Leaders were very angry about all this. So they arrested the Friends of Jesus again and put them in the common prison. But they escaped during the night, and by dawn they were back in the Temple, telling the Good News again to the people there.

While this was happening, the High Priest and the Jewish Leaders called the Council together, and sent for the prisoners. The police officers went to the prison, but the prisoners were no longer there. They went back without them.

'We found the prison safely locked all right,' they reported. 'The warders were on guard at the doors. When we unlocked the doors, we found nobody inside.'

When the Chief Constable and the members of the Council

heard this report, they had no idea what to do or what would happen next. Then someone came in with a report.

'The prisoners are back in the Temple, talking to the crowds,' he said.

The Chief Constable himself went to the Temple with police officers and brought them back to the court. They were very careful not to use any violence; they were afraid the crowd might start stoning them.

The Friends of Jesus faced the judges, and it was the High Priest who spoke.

'We gave you strict orders to stop talking about Jesus,' he said. 'Now everybody in the city is talking about him, and you're trying to make it look as if we were the people who killed him.'

'It's God's orders we must obey,' said Peter, 'not yours. The story we are telling is the plain truth. We are only talking about what we've seen for ourselves. God's power in us is proof of it too, the power he gives to all those who obey him.'

These words made them very angry and they wanted to pass the death sentence.

But one of the members of the Council stood up—Gamaliel, a lawyer who was deeply respected by the people of the city. He ordered the prisoners out of the courtroom for a few minutes.

'My fellow-countrymen,' he said, 'be careful what you are about to do with these men. We've had people like them before. There was Theudas; he set himself up as a leader of the people. Four hundred men joined him. But he got killed, and all his followers were scattered. The whole affair came to nothing. Then there was Judas—he came from Galilee too. He raised a rebellion, when the Romans were carrying out a census of the population here. He died, and all his followers were scattered. The point is this: keep your hands off these men and leave them alone. If this affair is just another popular uprising, it will come to nothing. If God is at the back of it, you can't stop these men—you'll be fighting against God himself!'

59

The Council agreed with him. They fetched the Friends of Jesus back into court and had them flogged. They ordered them to stop talking about Jesus, and then set them free again.

The Friends of Jesus left the court happy men, happy because it was for telling the story of Jesus that they had been treated so shamefully. But they didn't stop telling the people about him, either in the Temple or at home.

PALESTINE

About this time one of the Friends of Jesus, Stephen (whose story we shall tell later) told the Good News boldly in one of the city Meeting Houses. He could see what a different world Jesus wanted it to be, and he boldly said that all Jewish people must now change their way of life and begin to live in God's Way. Everything must be changed.

The Jewish Leaders arrested him and had him put to death. Other Friends of Jesus, who shared Stephen's point of view, were now also marked men and their lives too were in danger. So they escaped from the city, and went off to other towns and villages, some in Palestine itself, and some beyond its frontiers to other lands.

In this wider world they began to understand Jesus much more clearly.

We begin with those who went to other towns and villages in Palestine. Dr. Luke tells us two stories of a Friend of Jesus called Philip, to show us something of what happened there.

In Samaria

Philip escaped north to a city in Samaria and told the crowds there the story of Jesus.

They listened to him and watched his good deeds—sick people were cured and cripples walked again. Everybody felt that Philip was telling them the truth about God, and the city was a very happy city.

There was a magician, Simon, living there. For many years his magic had amazed everybody, in the city and far beyond it. He

called himself 'The Great Magician'. Members of the Government as well as the citizens were taken in by him.

'This man is indeed the Great Servant of God,' they said.

Now everything was changed. The people listened to Philip as he told them the Good News about God and the story of Jesus; many men and women became Friends of Jesus. Even Simon the magician became a Friend of Jesus and stayed with Philip. Philip's good deeds amazed even him.

News about all this came at last to the Christian Leaders in Jerusalem City.

They sent Peter and John to find out what was happening.

Nobody in Samaria had yet learned all that it meant to be a Friend of Jesus. So Peter and John held meetings for prayer, and asked God to give them his power. They put their hands on those who had become the Friends of Jesus—as a sign that God would give them his power—and God gave them his power.

Simon the magician was there and saw what happened. He brought some money and gave it to Peter and John.

, 'Show me how to do this,' he asked, 'so that I can put my hands on people too and get God to give them his power.'

'Take your money away!' said Peter. 'Do you think you can buy God's gift as you can buy magic—with money? You're no real Friend of Jesus; you haven't changed your heart at all. And what you've just done is a terrible thing. You must change the whole way you think and live, and you must ask God to forgive the thoughts that are in your heart, if possible. I can see how much of a magician you are still!'

'Pray to God for me,' said Simon, 'so that all the terrible things you've been talking about don't happen to me.'

Peter and John told the people again the story of Jesus and explained the Good News to them. Then they went home to Jerusalem City; and on their way they told the Good News in many of the villages of Samaria.

On the Desert Road

The Desert Road goes down from Jerusalem City to the plain and then on to Egypt.

One day, a high officer of the Queen of Upper Egypt, her Chief Treasurer, was riding in his carriage along the Desert Road. He had come all the way to Jerusalem City on pilgrimage, and was now going home. He was sitting in his carriage and reading the Bible aloud.

God had already spoken to Philip.

'At midday,' God had told him, 'be on the Desert Road.'

So Philip was on the road as the Chief Treasurer's carriage came along.

'Go up to this carriage,' said God, 'and join the traveller.'

Philip ran up to the carriage and heard the officer reading the Bible.

'Do you know what it all means?' he asked.

'How can I?' he said. 'I need someone to explain it to me.'

He invited Philip to climb up into the carriage and sit beside him.

The officer was reading the great poem in the Bible about God's Servant. Here is a verse of the poem:

As sheep on the way to the butcher
and lambs in the hands of a shearer make no noise;
   So God's Servant keeps quiet.
He was badly and unfairly treated,
Who will be able to talk about his descendants?
   for at last they killed him.

'My question is this,' said the officer. 'Who is he talking about? Is he talking about himself? Or is he talking about somebody else?'

This gave Philip his chance. He began by explaining the poem to the officer and went on to tell him the Good News of Jesus.

As they were going along the road, they came to some water.

'Look—there's water here,' said the officer. 'What's to stop me from joining the company of the Friends of Jesus here and now?'

He told the driver to stop the carriage. Both of them, Philip and the officer, went down to the water. Philip baptized him there and then; and the officer joined the company of the Friends of Jesus.

They came up out of the water. God had other work for Philip to do. The officer lost sight of him, but went on to Egypt a very happy man.

Philip turned up at a near-by town, Azotus, and then went on from town to town telling people the Good News. At last he came to the port of Caesarea, the headquarters of the Roman Army.

So far the Friends of Jesus have stayed in Palestine. They have been telling the Good News to the Jewish people, as Jesus did.

They now begin to realize that the Good News is for the whole world, not just for their own countrymen. Three men—Stephen, Peter and Paul—helped them to see how wide was the work that Jesus wanted them to do. The adventure Jesus called them to was a world adventure.

The Man who died for it : Stephen

We wish we knew more about Stephen, the first man to see that the Good News was for everybody everywhere and the first man to die, as a Friend of Jesus, in the world adventure. But all we know about him is what Dr. Luke tells us in the story which follows.

His Arrest

There were many Jewish people in Jerusalem City who had not been born in Palestine. They had come from their homes in such far away places as North Africa and Asia. They spoke Greek and read the Bible in Greek. Many were freed slaves or the sons of freed slaves. They had their own Meeting House in the city where they met together to worship God—the Freedmen's Meeting House. Most of them had come on pilgrimage. Some of these Jewish people had joined the company of the Friends of Jesus; and their leader was Stephen, a man who spoke, as Jesus had spoken, with such charm and power that people felt they had to listen.

Right : 'STORM AT SEA'. Autumn and winter were dangerous seasons for sailors. Ships spent the winter in harbour and waited for the calmer seas of spring. How Paul was caught in an autumn storm is told in 'How the Good News was brought to a "Barbarian" Island'.

Stephen told the Good News to these Jewish people from over-seas in their Meeting House. Many of them got up and argued with him, but they could not answer *his* arguments. He spoke sensibly and with God's power.

So they made secret plans. They spread rumours about him.

'We've heard him say terrible things about Moses who led us out of Egypt,' they whispered, 'and even about God himself!'

This made the Jewish people and their Leaders very angry indeed; and they arrested Stephen and dragged him off to the Jewish Council.

'This fellow never stops insulting the holy Temple and our religion,' they got men to lie. 'Why, we've even heard him say that this Jesus of Nazareth will knock this Temple down and change the way in which Moses taught us to live.'

All this time Stephen stood there, and members of the Council were sitting and staring at him, for there was an angelic look on his face.

'Is all this true?' asked the High Priest.

Stephen then spoke to the Council, and he had a lot to say.

His Defence

He told them their national story, how they became 'the People of God' in the days of Abraham and Joseph and Moses. He tried to make clear to them what God had really wanted them to be.

'Our ancestors,' he said, 'always worshipped God in a *tent*. God told Moses to set up a *tent* in the camp on the march across the desert, and they took it with them wherever they went. They set it

---

Left : ROME. If Athens was the most famous, Rome, the capital of the Empire, was the greatest city in the world. From here the world was governed, and here all roads met. There was a Christian community here very soon after the death of Jesus.

up here in Palestine, and here it stayed until David became King. It was only then we began to think about a *building* for God. It was King David who wanted to build a Temple for God. He didn't build it, you know; it was his son Solomon who built it.

'But you see what this means: God doesn't really live in buildings. The Bible puts it plainly—

> Heaven is my throne;
> earth is my footstool.
> What kind of house will you build for me,
> > says God,
> or where can I stay?
> Haven't I made everything in heaven and earth?

'Only the world is big enough for God, and we must live in his Way. But you Jewish people are always the same, as the Bible makes clear—you will never listen to God. You are just the same as your ancestors. Is there any Man of God your ancestors did not treat badly? They even killed the Men of God, although they were explaining God's Way and telling them how one day he would send his Chosen Leader. In our own day God *has* sent his Chosen Leader, and all you could do was to hand him over to the Romans and have him killed—you whom God himself has taught but who never did what he told you!'

They had listened quietly to him so far, but these last words made them wild with anger and they hissed at him. Stephen himself was filled with God's power and gazed over their heads. All he was thinking about and all he could see was—Jesus, full of God's glory and full of God's power.

'I see God's throne in heaven,' he said, 'and Jesus at God's right hand!'

The whole crowd broke into a great roar. They pressed their hands to their ears to shut out the sound of his voice; and in one great rush they tumbled over one another to get at him. They dragged him outside the city to stone him to death.

The men whose duty it was to see that he was really dead brought their clothes and put them down before a young officer of the court called Saul.

'Lord Jesus, receive me,' Stephen kept praying, even while they were throwing the stones at him.

He knelt down on the ground.

'O God,' he called out, 'forgive them this great wrong they are doing.'

It was all over. Saul was quite sure the right thing had been done.

That wasn't all that happened on that day, either. The crowds went off to get hold of other Friends of Jesus like Stephen, but they escaped into the country districts of Judea and Samaria. The close Friends of Jesus like Peter and John were left alone.

But Saul wanted more than the death of one man; he wanted to get rid of all the Friends of Jesus. He went from house to house, and dragged men and women off to prison.

The Man who began it : Peter

We have already seen how brave a man Peter was. He was not afraid of government or people, and he knew how dangerous it was to stand up in the Temple and tell the crowds the Good News about God 'in the name of Jesus'.

Yet he had not seen how wide God's love was and how big was the adventure Jesus had called him to. But one day he came to Caesarea, the headquarters of the Roman Army, and met a Roman Officer—a foreigner, not a Jew like himself. The officer, Captain Cornelius, was a good man who loved God and became a Friend of Jesus. It was then that Peter realized what Jesus had really cared for—the whole world, not just his own country of Palestine.

Lydda

Peter was going about the country visiting the Friends of Jesus. One day he went down from Jerusalem City to visit those who lived in the town of Lydda.

There he met a man called Aeneas, a cripple who had been in bed for eight long years.

'Aeneas,' said Peter, 'Jesus cures you. Get up and make your bed yourself.'

He stood straight up there and then.

All the people who lived in Lydda and the nearby town of Sharon saw for themselves that the man was strong and well again. That made them think seriously about the story of Jesus.

Joppa

In Joppa, a seaside town not far from Lydda, there lived a Friend of Jesus called Tabitha. She spent her time helping people in every way she could. She fell ill and died, and was laid in the room on the flat roof of the house.

The Friends of Jesus heard that Peter was at Lydda and they sent two men to tell him what had happened.

'Come across to us,' they said, 'and come quickly.'

Peter got up and went back with them; and when he got there they took him straight away up to the room on the roof. The widows whom Tabitha had helped crowded round him, with tears in their eyes, and showed him the coats and clothes which she had made when she was alive.

Peter had them all taken outside. He then knelt down and prayed. He turned toward the body.

'Tabitha, get up,' he said.

She opened her eyes. Then she saw Peter and sat up, and he gave her his hand and helped her to her feet. He called all the others into the room and showed them Tabitha—alive.

THE PORT OF JOPPA.

The news spread all over Joppa, and many people became Friends of Jesus. Peter stayed for quite a long time there, and made his home with Simon, a tanner.

Captain Cornelius

1. The Dream

Caesarea was the Headquarters of the Roman Army in Palestine, and among the officers there was a man called Cornelius, a captain of the Italian Regiment. He was a good man who, with all his family, loved God. He was always ready to help anybody in need and prayed to God every day.

One day, about three o'clock in the afternoon, he had a dream. Everything was very clear and he saw an angel of God coming towards him.

'Cornelius,' the angel called.

He stared at his visitor in terror.

'What's the matter, sir?' he asked.

'God knows all about you, your prayers and your good deeds,' he said. 'Send to Joppa and fetch a man called Simon—he's also known as Peter. He is staying with Simon the tanner; his house faces the sea.'

The angel left him.

Cornelius, without wasting a minute, called two of his slaves and one of his soldiers who loved God as he did, told them all about the dream and sent them off to Joppa.

2. Next Day

About noon next day, the three men were well on their way and had almost reached Joppa.

And it was about noon that Peter went up on to the flat roof of the house to pray. He suddenly felt hungry and wanted his dinner, but while the servants were getting it ready he fell asleep and started to dream.

It was a strange dream.

He saw something dropping down out of the open sky—something like a great sheet, tied at the four corners and being lowered to the earth. All sorts of animals and reptiles and wild birds were inside, including things no Jew, by Jewish law, was allowed to eat.

He heard a Voice speaking.

'Get up, Peter,' it said, 'kill them and eat them.'

'Never, sir,' said Peter. 'I've never eaten any forbidden food.'

'What God calls good food,' said the Voice, 'you mustn't call forbidden food.'

This happened three times. Then the thing was suddenly drawn up into the sky.

While Peter was wondering what the dream could mean, the messengers of Cornelius stood outside the gate; all this time they had been asking people the way to Simon's house.

THE PORT OF CAESAREA, the headquarters of the Roman Governor.

'Is Simon, called Peter, staying here?' they called out.

Peter was still up on the roof, wondering about the dream.

'There are three men looking for you,' God told him. 'Get up and go down to them and go along with them. There's nothing to worry about; I've sent them.'

Peter went down to the men.

'I am the man you are looking for,' he said. 'What have you come for?'

'We come from Captain Cornelius, a good man who loves God—all the Jews in Caesarea will tell you that. He was told by God to invite you to his house, and to listen to what you have to say.'

Peter asked them to stay with him. Next morning, he got up and went off with them; and some of the Friends of Jesus in Joppa went along with him.

3. At Caesarea

They got to Caesarea the next day.

Captain Cornelius had asked his relatives and close friends to come along, and was looking out for Peter and the three men. He met Peter as he was entering the house, and fell down on the ground in front of him; he thought Peter must be no ordinary man.

Peter pulled him to his feet.

'Stand up,' he said, 'I'm an ordinary man like yourself.'

Talking with Cornelius, he went on into the crowded house.

'You all know about Jewish Law,' he said. 'You know it forbids a Jew to have anything to do with a foreigner—even to visit him. But I now know better, for God has made it quite clear to me that I must not call anybody at all, whoever he is, "foreigner". I couldn't say No when you sent for me. Tell me why you wanted me to come.'

Captain Cornelius told him about his dream.

'So, you see,' he said, 'I sent at once to invite you and you have kindly come along. All of us in this room know God is here, and we want to listen to what God has told you to tell us.'

'It's as clear as daylight to me now', said Peter, 'that God has no favourites. It doesn't matter what race or nation you belong to; if you love God and do what is right, God welcomes you.

'You know what the Bible says—

He sent out his word and healed them.

and

THE ROMAN THEATRE AT CAESAREA. It is used today, and the photograph shows a play being performed there.

How lovely on the hills
   are the footsteps of the man who brings the Good News
   and calls all the world to be at peace.

'All this is really about Jesus.

'He is God's Chosen Leader; all the world is his Kingdom, and he has brought the Good News of peace.

'You yourselves, too, know something about what has happened in Palestine in our own time—the events that began in Galilee after John the Hermit had been preaching in Jordan Valley, and the story of Jesus from Nazareth Village.

'Let me tell you what really happened.

'God called Jesus to his great work, and gave him his Spirit and power. He went from village to village doing good and healing sick people; for God was with him. We saw with our own eyes all he did in Palestine and in Jerusalem City.

'He died on a Roman cross; but God soon raised him from the dead—the same Jesus we had known in Galilee. The crowds didn't see him; only those whom God had chosen saw him—we who had dinner with him when he was alive again. He told us what to do: to tell the Good News to everybody, and to make it quite clear that, in all he said and did, God has shown us what is right and what is wrong. Jesus, not Caesar or Moses, is the judge of all men everywhere. Everybody who trusts in Jesus is forgiven for all the wrong things he has done—because he was what he was. This is surely what the Bible tells us.'

Peter was still speaking when God's power was given to everybody who had been listening to him. The Jewish Friends of Jesus who had come along with Peter were amazed—fancy God giving his power even to *foreigners*! They themselves heard them, there in the room, singing God's praises!

'God has given his power to these foreigners just as he gave it to us Jews,' said Peter. 'Can anybody say they ought not to join the company of the Friends of Jesus?'

He gave orders for them to be baptized 'in the name of Jesus'.

Afterwards they all wanted Peter to stay a few days in Caesarea.

4. Back in Jerusalem

News about what had happened in Caesarea reached the Jewish Friends of Jesus in Jerusalem and the south—foreigners had become Friends of Jesus!

Some of them thought this was wrong. Only Jews, they thought, could become Friends of Jesus; if foreigners wanted to, they should become Jews first. So when Peter went up to Jerusalem City, they took the matter up with him.

'Why did you meet foreigners,' they said bitterly, 'and share their home-life?'

Peter told them the whole story—his dream at Joppa and what happened in the home of Captain Cornelius.

'Then I remembered the words of Jesus,' he went on. 'He said, you remember, "John the Hermit used water as a sign; God will give you, my Friends, his own power in your hearts". God gave these foreigners in Caesarea his own power in their hearts. If God gave to them, foreigners though they were, the same gift that he gave to us when *we* became the Friends of Jesus, who was I to say No to God himself?'

When they heard Peter talk like this, they had nothing more to say.

'Foreigners also can change their ways,' they said, 'and live in God's Way!'

And they praised God.

Trouble Again

Herod again arrested some of the Friends of Jesus. He had James, the brother of John, beheaded. This made him popular. So he looked round for others, and, during the Great Feast, arrested Peter as well. After his arrest, he put him in prison with sixteen soldiers on guard. He planned to parade him before the people when the Feast was over. All the Friends of Jesus could do was to pray for him, and this they did day and night.

The Feast was over and the very next day Herod had planned to bring Peter out and show him to the crowds. It was late at night. Peter was asleep. Two soldiers lay on either side of him and he was handcuffed to them. Outside the prison door, sentries stood on guard.

A light shone in the cell and a messenger from God stood there. He tapped Peter on his side and woke him up.

'Get up quickly,' he said.

The handcuffs fell from his wrists.

'Fasten your belt,' he said, 'and put your sandals on.'

Peter did what he was told.

'Put your cloak on and follow me.'

Peter followed him out. It was like a dream; it didn't seem real. They passed the first sentry, then the second sentry, and came to the great iron gate. Beyond the gate lay the city. Nobody was there, but the gate swung open. They went through, and along the narrow street. The messenger vanished.

By this time Peter was wide awake.

'Now I know God has rescued me,' he said to himself, 'rescued me from Herod and the show the crowds were looking forward to.'

He realised what had happened, and off he went to the house of Mary, John Mark's mother, where many Friends of Jesus were meeting to pray for him.

He knocked on the door of the outer gate, and Rhoda, a maid, came to see who it was. She knew at once it was Peter's voice. Back she ran to tell everybody—she didn't stop to open the door, she was so happy.

'Peter's outside the door,' she burst out.

'You're mad,' they told her.

'It *is* Peter!' said Rhoda.

'It's his ghost,' they said.

Peter went on knocking.

At last they opened the door, and, to their amazement, there was Peter himself!

With a wave of his hand, he got them to be quiet, and told them how God had rescued him from prison.

'Tell James and the other Friends of Jesus,' he said.

Then he left them and went away.

There was great alarm among the soldiers when daylight came. They hadn't any idea what had become of Peter. Herod ordered a search for him, but he was nowhere to be found. He had the guards examined and ordered them to be executed. Then he went down from Jerusalem to his palace at Caesarea.

The Man who led the Adventure: Paul

When Dr. Luke was telling us about Stephen and how he died, he gave the name of the 'young officer of the court' who was in charge of the execution. His name was Saul, and he hated all the Friends of Jesus. It is this man who is going to be the hero of Dr. Luke's book. For, not long after, he himself became a Friend of Jesus.

This is the story of how it happened near the city of Damascus.

Saul is a Jewish name. It was the name of the first Hebrew King, and boys of the Benjamin Clan would be proud to be called Saul. Saul was born a Roman citizen, so he had a Roman name, Paul, as well as his Jewish name. Perhaps his full name was Gaius Julius Paulus. Later in the book Dr. Luke uses his Roman name, and this Roman name, Paul, is the one by which he is best known.

On the Road

Saul was hot on the trail of the Friends of Jesus, thirsting for their blood. He went to the High Priest and asked him for warrants to search the Meeting Houses in Damascus, to arrest all 'the People of God's Way'—as the Friends of Jesus called themselves—and to bring them, men and women alike, as prisoners to Jerusalem City.

He set off along the Damascus Road.

He had almost reached his journey's end when, suddenly, a light from the sky burst on him and he fell down on the road. He heard a Voice.

'Saul! Saul!' the Voice called. 'Why do you treat me like an enemy?'

'Who are you?' asked Saul.

'I am Jesus—and you are treating me like an enemy! But get up and go on into Damascus City. You'll get your orders there.'

His fellow-travellers stood speechless with fright; they heard the Voice, but they saw nobody.

Saul got up. When he tried to see where he was, he found he was blind; they had to lead him by the hand into the city. For three days he was blind and had nothing to eat or drink.

In Damascus

A Friend of Jesus, Ananias, was living in Damascus City. He had a dream, and in the dream he saw Jesus.

'Ananias!' said Jesus.

'I'm here, Lord,' he answered.

'Get up,' said Jesus, 'and go to Straight Street. Find the house where Judas lives, and ask for Saul, a citizen of Tarsus City. You'll find him praying. He's had a dream, and in his dream he has seen a man called Ananias enter the house and put his hands on his eyes and give him his sight back again.'

'Lord,' said Ananias, 'I've heard all sorts of stories about this man; he's here with a warrant to arrest all your Friends in the city.'

'Off you go,' said Jesus. 'I've marked him out as my messenger. His orders are to tell the whole world the Good News—foreigners and their governments as well as Jewish people. And I'll not hide from him the dangers he'll have to face as a Friend of mine.'

Ananias went off and found the house and put his hands on Saul.

'Brother Saul,' he said, 'It was the Lord Jesus you saw on the road outside the city. He has sent me to you. May you have your sight back again, and may you be filled with God's power!'

His sight came back—as suddenly as he had lost it—and he could see quite clearly.

He got up, and Ananias baptized him and received him into the company of the Friends of Jesus. He had a good meal and felt quite well again.

He stayed with the Friends of Jesus for a few days. The first thing he did was to go along to the Meeting House—and tell them the story of Jesus!

'He *is* God's Son,' he said.

Everybody, listening to him talk, was amazed.

'Isn't this the man who tried to wipe out the Friends of Jesus in Jerusalem City? they asked. 'Why, he came here with a warrant for the arrest of those who live here, to take them back as prisoners to our Leaders.'

This didn't stop Saul. He spoke all the more powerfully in the Meeting Houses. He shocked the Jewish people in the city—they didn't know how to answer his arguments. He had only one thing to say—Jesus is God's Chosen Leader.

This went on for quite a time. At last the Jewish people plotted to murder him, and they picketed the city gates the whole twenty-four hours of the day. Somebody told Saul about the plot; and one night his friends took him to the city wall, and lowered him over the wall in a basket.

To Jerusalem and Tarsus

Saul went back to Jerusalem. He tried to get in touch with the Friends of Jesus there; but they were afraid of him. They thought he was just pretending to be a Friend of Jesus.

But Barnabas introduced him to the Christian Leaders. He told them how Saul had seen Jesus on the Damascus Road and been given his orders, and how he had told the Good News boldly in the Meeting Houses of Damascus City.

That settled it, and he was welcomed into all their homes. He showed the same boldness in talking about Jesus in Jerusalem

City as he had in Damascus City. His chief aim was to meet the Jews from overseas and argue with them; but they, like the Damascus Jews, made up their minds to murder him.

Somebody told the Friends of Jesus about the plot, and they took him down to the port of Caesarea and sent him off home to Tarsus City.

The Great Plan

Dr. Luke now leaves Palestine and takes us to Antioch City in the north. This was a large and famous city, and roads from north, south, east and west met there. It was not an old city; it had been built, two hundred or more years before, in honour of King Antiochus.

After the death of Stephen, some of his friends escaped to Antioch, and, later, Friends of Jesus from other lands came to live there. All these men believed that Jesus cared for everybody, not just for Jewish people. Antioch was crowded with people from many lands, and these Friends of Jesus began to tell the Good News to anybody who would listen, without bothering whether they were Jews or not.

Then one day, in a prayer meeting, they were sure that God wanted them to begin to take the Good News all over the world. They made up their minds to plan this great work. This is the story of what happened, and how Paul comes into it.

The *first* great day in the story of the Friends of Jesus was the day when, in Jerusalem City, they received God's power to live in his Way (p. 52); this is the *second* great day in their story—and, it is important to note, it takes place on foreign soil.

How the Good News came to Antioch City

After the death of Stephen, many of the Friends of Jesus were scattered, as we have seen. Some of them went to Phoenicia, where ships set sail for Africa and Italy and Spain. Some went to the

---

Left : DAMASCUS CITY—the Gateway leading to Straight Street.

Island of Cyprus, the homeland of Barnabas. Some went to Antioch City in the north, the third greatest city of the Empire, where the great roads from Europe and Egypt and Babylon met. It was in this city that the Friends of Jesus made the great plan to take the Good News all over the world, to foreigners and Jewish people alike. This is how it happened.

At first, the Friends of Jesus in Antioch City told the Good News to Jewish people only. But Friends of Jesus from the island of Cyprus and from North Africa came to live there; and *they* began to tell the story of Jesus to Greek people, foreigners, not Jews. This was clearly what God wanted them to do, for many of the Greek foreigners believed the Good News and became Friends of Jesus.

News of all this reached Jerusalem City, and the Leaders of the Friends of Jesus there sent Barnabas off to Antioch to find out what was happening. When he got there, he saw what a difference God's love had made to them all; and he was very glad.

'You've made up your minds to be Friends of Jesus,' he told them. 'Stick to it, and don't let Jesus down.'

He was a good man, full of God's power, and he trusted God with his whole heart.

The company of the Friends of Jesus grew. So Barnabas set off for Tarsus City to find Saul, and brought him back with him to Antioch. For a whole year they met the Friends of Jesus there in their meetings together, and explained the story of Jesus to a large company of people. It was in this city that the Friends of Jesus were first nicknamed 'Christians'—'Christ's Men'.

The Great Decision

Now in the company of the Friends of Jesus, there were leaders who explained the meaning of the Bible and leaders who explained the meaning of all that Jesus said and did. These are their names: Barnabas, Simon the 'Black', Luke from North Africa, Manaen

Right : ANTIOCH CITY.

82

who had been the close friend of King Herod, and Saul. One day they were meeting for prayer and fasting.

'I have called Barnabas and Saul to a great work,' God said to them. 'Give them this work to do.'

They went on with their prayers and fasting, asking God to guide them. Then they sent Barnabas and Saul to tell the Good News to the people of the Empire.

From East to West

The Friends of Jesus in Antioch City did not know what a great adventure they were beginning, an adventure which was to spread all over the world and go on all down the centuries. It is going on still today.

Two men started out from Antioch, Barnabas and Saul. Saul was the great leader.

Dr. Luke now begins the story of Saul and his journeys across the world. (From now on we will use his Roman name—Paul.) We shall tell this story in our next book, *Paul the Explorer*. Here we tell six of Dr. Luke's stories to show how the Good News was taken all over the world, until at last, one spring day, Paul walked into the capital city of the Roman Empire, Rome itself.

As the Friends of Jesus walked along the roads of the Empire, climbed the mountains and sailed the seas, they began at last to understand Jesus. As they told the Good News to everybody they met, and men and women everywhere listened to it and became Friends of Jesus, they knew why Jesus had lived and died and been raised to life again. They remembered his words, and they followed his example.

So we shall find ourselves in Greek and 'barbarian' islands, in famous cities and country towns high in the mountains, and at last we shall enter the gates of Rome itself. Everybody everywhere matters.

Right: THE ISLAND OF CYPRUS. Here Barnabas and Paul began 'the great adventure' of taking the Good News to the whole world. It was where Barnabas had grown up as a boy and he would know it well.

Barnabas and Paul set off. They were now sure that this was the work God had given them to do.

They went down to the port of Seleucia, took ship for Cyprus and landed at Salamis Town, in the eastern part of the island. John Mark went along with them to help them.

They told the story of Jesus in the Jewish Meeting Houses, and in this way they went through the whole island.

They came at last to Paphos on the west coast, where the Roman Governor, Sergius Paul, had his headquarters. Here they met a Jewish magician, called Bar Jesus, who was friendly with the Governor.

The Governor was a thoughtful man, and when he heard about Barnabas and Paul, he asked them to come to see him. He wanted to hear the story of Jesus. Bar Jesus the magician was there, and tried to prove to the Governor that they were wrong; he didn't want to lose his job.

Paul (his Roman name was the same as the Governor's) was filled with God's power and looked straight at the magician.

'There isn't a trick or a lie in your trade you don't know,' he said. 'You're a bad man. You'd twist anything for gain—even religion! But you're dealing with God not men; you shall be blind for a time —you won't even see the brightness of the sun!'

Suddenly, the magician's world went misty and dark, and he had to feel his way about and get people to lead him by the hand.

The Governor watched all this, and became a Friend of Jesus. But what amazed him was the story of Jesus.

How the Good News came to the Highlands of Anatolia

Barnabas and Paul came one day to the old town of Lystra, high up in the highlands of Anatolia, where people, though they could speak Greek, usually spoke their own strange language which Paul and Barnabas couldn't understand.

There was a man here who had been a cripple all his life and had never been able to walk.

Paul was talking to the crowd near the town gates and the cripple sat there on the roadside listening to him. Paul looked straight at him and saw the man believed he could cure him.

'Get up on your feet!' said Paul, loudly enough for everybody to hear. 'Stand up straight!'

The cripple jumped up and walked about.

The crowd saw what Paul had done, and they started shouting in their own strange language.

'The gods have come down like men and here they are in our city!' they said.

They thought Barnabas was the great god Zeus, and Paul the messenger of the gods, Hermes—because he did all the talking!

The priest of Zeus, who looked after the nearby temple called 'The Temple of Zeus-outside-the-Town', brought bulls wreathed with flowers to the town gates, to sacrifice to Barnabas and Paul as gods.

Barnabas and Paul couldn't help but hear all this noise. When they saw what it all meant, they tore their clothes and ran among the crowd.

'Sirs!' they shouted. 'What's all this for? We are just ordinary men like you, and all we're doing is bringing you Good News. Stop all this nonsense and learn what God is really like. He's the Living God; he made the sky and land and seas. He made the whole world. Until now God let people everywhere do what they thought best. Yet even then he showed you what he was like. He looked after you all. He gave you rain from the sky and harvest time. He saw that you had food to eat. All your happiness comes from him.'

Even words like this hardly stopped the crowd from going on with their sacrifice.

THE HIGHLANDS OF ANATOLIA.

Then Jews from the towns where Paul and Barnabas had already been came along and told the crowd what *they* thought about them. That turned the crowd against Paul and Barnabas, and they started throwing stones at Paul. They thought they had killed him, and dragged him outside the town.

Paul's friends stood round him; they, too, thought he was dead. But he got up and went back into the town.

How the Good News came to a Jewish Meeting House

Paul and his friend Silas came one day to the town of Beroea in northern Greece. They had been travelling through the night, and when they reached the town they went into the Jewish Meeting House.

The Jewish people here were better mannered than those in other towns they had visited. They listened to the story of Jesus gladly, and every day they read the Bible carefully to see if what Paul said was true. Many became Friends of Jesus, and among them were well-known Greek women and quite a number of men. But the Jewish people in the city from which Paul had come heard that he was now telling the Good News in Beroea, and they came across to cause trouble and set the mob against him.

The Friends of Jesus there at once got Paul off on his way to the sea. Silas and Timothy stayed behind, and Paul's guides took him by boat as far as the city of Athens.

How the Good News came
to the most Famous Greek City of all

Paul came to Athens by boat, and he was waiting there for Silas and Timothy.

He wandered through the streets; everywhere there were temples and images of the Greek gods. This made Paul very unhappy. He had to talk to somebody about it. He went to the Jewish Meeting House and argued there; he went to the Market Place and argued with anybody who happened to be there. There were many lecturers in the city, for its university was very famous; some of them met Paul, and he argued with them.

'What's this chatterer talking about?' sneered some.

'It's some foreign fellow talking about his gods, it seems,' said others.[1]

The City Council was called 'Mars Hill', after the name of the hill where it used to meet in earlier times. This Council was specially interested in all new speakers who came to teach in Athens. The

---

[1] Paul had been talking, of course, about Jesus and how he was risen from the dead. The word he used here was 'Anastasis' which simply means 'rising from the dead'; the lecturers thought it was the name of another foreign god!

citizens of Athens and their foreign visitors always had time to talk about or listen to anything strange and new; they seemed to do nothing else.

The lecturers got hold of Paul and took him before the Council.

'Tell us, if you please, something more about this "News" of yours,' they said. 'What you've been talking about sounds very strange to us. We'd like to know what it's all about.'

Paul stood before the Council.

'Citizens of Athens,' he said, 'by just wandering around your streets, I can see that religion matters very much to you. I had a good look at your temples and the images of your gods. And I noticed one altar that had these words on it "To an Unknown God". You do not know him; I will tell you about him.

'The God who made the world and all that's in it by that very fact is the Master of the whole world. His home can't be a temple in a street that you can build with your own hands.[1] He can't need temple servants, as though he had to have somebody looking after him. He gave us the very lives we live and everything we have. We may belong to different nations now, but at the beginning God made us all one people and gave us the whole world for our home. All things are in his hands—the rise and fall of nations and the boundaries of their territories. He did all this for one purpose only— that men and women might look for him and find him.

'Yet he is very near every one of us. Your own poets have said this very thing—

In God we live and move and exist,

and

We, too, belong to his family.

'If, therefore, we belong to God, we can't possibly think that gold and silver and stone are good enough to show us what he is like. No artist can paint God's picture, however clever or thoughtful he may be.

[1] See the speech of Stephen (p. 65).

90

'THE MOST FAMOUS GREEK CITY OF ALL'—ATHENS. The photograph shows the great temple on the high hill called the Acropolis

'What, then, has God done? He takes no notice of the past, when we didn't know what he is like. But today, in our own time, he calls all people to change their ways. We can no longer say we do not know; Jesus has made him plain. The day is fixed when everybody everywhere will be judged by this man he has chosen— and truly judged. The proof of this he has given to all men—he has raised him from the dead.'

Some of them laughed out loud at Paul when they heard him talk like this—about God 'raising Jesus from the dead'. But there were others.

'We'll hear you again about all this,' they said.

So Paul left them.

But there were some who went along with Paul and became Friends of Jesus. Among them were Dionysius, a member of the City Council itself, and a woman whose name was Damaris.

How the Good News came to a 'Barbarian' Island
(The Diary)

Sailing to Rome

This story begins in Palestine, and in the port of Caesarea, the headquarters of the Roman army.

The Roman Governor decided to send us by ship to Italy. He put Paul and some other prisoners in the care of Captain Julius of the Imperial Regiment whose officers served as messengers between the Emperor and his armies. There was a boat in harbour which came from a port near Troas; it was about to sail home, calling at places along the coast on the way. We went on board and set sail.

Next day we called at Sidon. Captain Julius was very good to Paul and let him visit the Friends of Jesus there and be cared for.

We put to sea again and sailed under the shelter of the island of Cyprus, for the north-west winds were blowing against us. We left the shelter of the island and sailed across the open sea to the mainland, and came to the port of Myra. There Captain Julius found an Egyptian grain-ship bound for Italy and put us on board. There were two hundred and seventy-six passengers.

For many days we sailed slowly westward, and it took us all our time to get as far as Cnidus. The wind was too strong to let us go on across the open sea; so we sailed southward round the island of Crete, where we were sheltered from the wind. It was hard enough sailing along the coast of the island, but we came at last to a small bay called Fair Havens, not far from a city. There we dropped anchor.

Right : MOUNT IDA IN THE ISLAND OF CRETE. It was here that the sailors on Paul's ship wanted to spend the winter.

We had wasted a lot of time, and the dangerous season for ships had begun, when great storms blow up. Even the Jewish Feast, which took place on October 5th, was over.

Paul spoke to Captain Julius and the pilot and the ship-owner. 'Gentlemen,' he said, 'if we put to sea again now, I can see we shall run into great danger; we shall lose not only the cargo and the ship but our own lives as well.'

But Captain Julius listened more to the pilot and the ship-owner than to Paul.

The harbour at Fair Havens, it was true, was not a good place to spend the winter in. Most of the officers on board were for putting to sea and trying to get to the port of Phoenix to spend the winter there. (This was the only safe harbour, in all winds, on the south coast of Crete; it faces away from the winds, north-east and south-east.)

The Great Storm

One day the wind blew gently from the southwest. Now was their chance. They weighed anchor and sailed close along the coast of Crete. Suddenly a gale, called 'The Northeaster', blew down from the land. The ship was caught and could not face the wind.

So we ran before it and were driven out to sea. We ran under the shelter of the small island of Cauda, and even then had a hard job to get the ship's boat safely tied up on deck. The sailors fastened ropes over and under the ship to stop her from breaking up. They were frightened that they might be driven southward on to the African quicksands; they put out a sea anchor, but were still swept along.

We were tossed so violently about by the storm that next day the sailors began to throw the cargo overboard. On the third day, they threw away with their own hands everything they could. For many days we saw neither sun nor stars; we were at the mercy of the storm. At last we gave up hope of ever being saved.

All this time crew and passengers hadn't bothered to eat. So Paul stood up and spoke to them all.

'Gentlemen,' he said, 'you should have listened to me. You shouldn't have sailed from Crete; you wouldn't, then, have had such damage and lost so much. But now I'm going to tell you something to cheer you up.

'You'll lose the ship, but none of you will lose your lives. I had a dream last night. A messenger of the God to whom I belong and whom I serve stood by me. "Don't be frightened, Paul," he said. "You must stand before the Emperor. God has saved the lives of all those who are sailing with you." So cheer up, my friends. I trust God that it will all happen just as I've been told. But we shall be ship-wrecked on some island.'

Shipwreck

A fortnight passed, and all the time we were drifting across the open sea.

One night—it was about midnight—the sailors guessed that we were getting near land. They dropped the lead overboard and found we were in twenty fathoms of water. When we had sailed a little farther, they dropped the lead again—this time it was fifteen fathoms. They were now frightened that we might run on to the rocks; so they threw out four anchors from the stern, and prayed for daylight.

The sailors wanted to abandon ship, and lowered the small boat into the sea.

'We only want to let the anchors down from the bow,' they lied.

Paul spoke to Captain Julius and the soldiers.

'If these men don't stay on board,' he said, 'none of you will get ashore.'

The soldiers cut the boat's ropes and let it fall into the sea.

Just before dawn, Paul told them all to get a good meal.

'For a fortnight you've been so scared you haven't bothered to eat anything. You're starving. If you'll listen to me, you'll get something inside you—you'll need it if you're going to get ashore safely. I've told you—you'll not lose a hair of your head.'

With these words, he picked up a loaf, said Grace over it while they all watched, broke it and began to eat it. They all cheered up and had a good breakfast. When everybody had eaten enough, they threw the cargo of wheat into the sea to make the ship ride lighter.

Daylight came, but they couldn't tell where they were; they could see a small bay with a sandy beach—just the place, if they could get to it, to run the ship ashore. They let the anchors go and left them in the sea; and loosed the ropes that held the rudders fast. A breeze was blowing. They set the foresail, and made for the shore.

They ran into rough water where two strong currents met and drove the ship aground. The bow stuck fast and nothing could move it; while the stern, beaten by the great seas, began to break up. The soldiers were for killing the prisoners—they thought they might swim off and escape Captain Julius stopped that; Paul was an important prisoner and he didn't want him killed. He told those who could swim to jump into the sea first and get ashore, and the others, on cargo boards or bits of wreckage, to get there as best as they could. So it was that everybody got safely to the beach.

On the Island of Malta

When we had all reached the beach, we found out where we were —the island of Malta. The natives didn't treat us as we expected, but showed us every kindness. It was beginning to rain and everybody was very cold; so they lit a bonfire and made us all feel at home.

Paul picked up a bundle of brushwood to put on the fire. There was a viper in it and the heat woke it up; it got hold of his hand and was hanging from it. The natives were watching.

THE ISLAND OF MALTA—the bay where Paul was shipwrecked.

'The fellow's a murderer,' they said to one another. 'He may have escaped drowning, but the Goddess of Justice has seen to it that he won't get away with it.'

Paul shook the viper off into the fire. The natives waited—surely he would swell up or suddenly fall down dead. Nothing happened. They went on waiting and watching; and still nothing happened. That changed their minds.

'He's a god himself,' they said.

The Chief of the island, a man called Publius, owned all the lands round about the bay. He welcomed us and looked after us for three days in a most friendly way. His father was very ill with fever at the time. Paul went to see him, prayed for him, put his hands on him and cured him. Then everybody else who was ill came along, and Paul cured them too. Nothing was too much for the people to do for us. And when we went on board ship to leave the island, they gave us everything we needed.

How the Good News came to the Capital of the Empire

It was three months before we left.

In February we went on board another Egyptian ship which had spent the winter at the island; she had 'The Heavenly Twins' as her figure-head. We put in at the port of Syracuse. The wind dropped and we had to spend three days there. We weighed anchor at last, and made for the port of Rhegium. The south wind started blowing next day, and it took us only two days to get to Puteoli, one of the ports for Rome.

We looked up the Friends of Jesus in the town, and they asked us to spend a week with them. Then we set off for Rome.

The Friends of Jesus in the city had heard we were coming and came out to meet us—more than forty miles, as far as the Market Town of Appius and The Three Inns.

When Paul saw them he thanked God and felt ready for anything.

We came at last into Rome itself.

Paul was allowed to hire a house outside the barracks and live there by himself with a soldier on guard.

He had been there only three days when he asked the Jewish Leaders in the city to meet him, and they came along.

'I want to tell you about myself, brothers,' he said. 'I have done nothing against the Jewish people or the customs of our ancestors. Yet I was handed over as a prisoner to the Romans. This happened in Jerusalem. The Romans, after a long trial, wanted to set me free—I had done nothing, they found, to deserve the death sentence. The Jews wouldn't have it. So there was only one thing to do—appeal to the Emperor. But I have no complaint to make against my own people.

Right: THE APPIAN WAY, the ancient road to Rome. This was the road along which Paul travelled from the port of Puteoli to Rome.

'That is why I asked you to come to see me and let me talk to you. It is because of the hope my people have held for hundreds of years that I am wearing these handcuffs.'

'We haven't had any letters from Palestine about you,' they said, 'and nobody who has come here has said anything against you. We would like to hear what you've got to say. All we know about the Friends of Jesus is that everybody says they're a bad lot.'

They fixed on a day for meeting Paul, and a great crowd came to his house. He talked about God's Way. He told them the story of Jesus and tried to show them that this is what the Bible was about. He went on talking all day.

Some of them thought he was right, and some of them thought he was wrong. They couldn't agree with one another and that ended the meeting. Paul had the last word.

'You are doing just what our people have done all down the centuries. We will not listen to what God has got to say. Well, be quite sure of this: it is to foreigners everywhere the Good News about God has been sent—they will listen.'

Paul stayed for two whole years in the house he had rented. He let anybody come to see him who wanted to. He spent his time telling the Good News and explaining the story of Jesus. He did this quite openly; nobody stopped him.

Right: THE CAPITAL OF THE EMPIRE—ROME. The photograph shows part of the Forum, the city square. Here the Emperor lived, and from here the whole Empire was governed. Here Paul wanted to spend a short holiday on his way to Spain. But when he came here, he came as a prisoner, guarded by Roman soldiers.

Things to do[1]

PART ONE—THE PIONEER

WHEN YOU HAVE READ 'WHICH WAY?' (p. 20).

Jesus had to think things out, as we do. What did God want him to do? When he told his Friends about these long days on the lonely moorland, he put it into pictures like his stories. This is what we often do when we try to tell somebody what we are thinking; we say 'It is like . . .'.

We do not know when Jesus told his Friends about his thoughts while he was out on the moors alone. Perhaps he told his three Friends, Peter, James and John, when he was walking up the mountain with them (*The Beginning*, p. 49).

Drawing and Painting

Illustrate the pictures Jesus gives us: 1. On the rocky moorland; 2. Looking down from the high mountain (remember Jesus had grown up in a mountain village which looked down on a wide plain; and from the moorlands he could see far across Jordan Valley to the eastern mountains); 3. On the Gate of the Temple. Write underneath what you think Jesus wanted these stories to help his Friends to understand.

Writing

Write an account of the conversation between Jesus and his friends on the walk up the mountain. (Remember what had happened a week before— *The Beginning*, 'On a Country Road' p. 49—when he and Peter had disagreed about what God wanted him to do.)

---

[1] For some of the information you will need to consult your local Public Library.

Talking

Discuss together what you think these stories Jesus told his Friends mean and how they help us to understand what Jesus decided to do when he began his work in Galilee. What *could* he have done?

How do these stories of Jesus help us when we have to think things out and make difficult decisions?

WHEN YOU HAVE READ 'DANGERS AHEAD' (p. 21)

Drawing and Painting

Make pictures of the three stories showing how Jesus was treated in his own village, by King Herod, and in the foreign village: 1. Jesus in Nazareth; 2. King Herod tells his soldiers to arrest Jesus; 3. The Friends of Jesus are sent away from the Village.

Acting or Miming

Make a short play or plan a mime on one of these stories: Jesus visits Nazareth; 'The Scene in Herod's Palace'; 'What happened at the Gate of the Village and afterward'. If you write the plays, you could put them on a tape-recorder for the class to hear.

Finding Things out

1. Find out what a service in a Jewish Meeting House was like. If you live near a Jewish Synagogue, ask your teacher if he could arrange for your class to visit it; then you can ask the Rabbi himself. There are records of Jewish music.

2. Can you find out which city King Herod lived in? He was building a new city at the time. Can you find out where this city was?

3. The 'foreign' village was in Samaria. Find out from the map where Samaria and Galilee were. Many Jews would not go through Samaria; how would they get from Galilee to Jerusalem without going through Samaria?

4. Can you find any stories about Christians facing danger as Jesus did? (For example, Francis of Assisi, William Tyndale, John Woolman,

George Fox, John Wesley, General Booth; Christians in China and India and Africa as well as Europe and America).

Writing

Dr. Luke was in Palestine when Paul was arrested, and met many Friends of Jesus who had been with Jesus in Galilee. Imagine you were Dr. Luke; write an account of Dr. Luke interviewing Peter who was with Jesus in Nazareth when the incident took place (p. 21).

WHEN YOU HAVE READ
'THE PLAN OF THE VENTURE: HIS FRIENDS' (p. 24).

Drawing or Painting

Although Jesus spent most of his time among his own countrymen, he cared for the whole world. In so big an adventure he needs Friends to help him. Make a frieze of pictures—or a book of pictures—to illustrate how the Friends of Jesus have helped him: Friends in Galilee; and Friends of different races and peoples all over the world. Write a short account of each of them to go under each picture.

Acting or Miming

Find out a story about someone who carried on the work of Jesus: in India, in Africa, or in America; e.g., Sadhu Sundar Singh (India); the Prophet Harris (Africa); John Woolman and the Indians (America). Make your own short play or mime about an incident in their lives.

If you are a girl, what about a play or mime called 'The Two Sisters' (Martha and Mary, p. 28)?

Writing

1. Friends like Peter helped Jesus in Palestine; write an account of how Peter helped Jesus. Find out a story of someone who helped Jesus in China; *or* in the South Sea Islands; write your own account of how he or she helped Jesus there.

2. Write an account of the different ways in which the Friends of Jesus can help him (it isn't just talkers that Jesus wants). How can a nurse or a

farmer or an engineer help him? Ask your teacher if you could write to a Missionary Society and ask them in how many different ways their missionaries help Jesus.

3. Write an account of how one of the churches in your town or village carries on the work of Jesus (you could write to its minister or one of its officers).

Finding Things out

1. What kind of work do you think Jesus wants his Friends to do in your town or village? Find out who is doing it.

2. Find out the story of someone who has carried on the work of Jesus in your own country. Who was he? Whad did he (or she) do?

3. Find out in what ways one of the churches in your town or village carries on the work of Jesus.

4. Find out who first brought the Good News to China; to India; *or* to America; *or* to East Africa.

Questions to discuss

1. Why does the work Jesus is doing need the help of his Friends?
2. In what ways can the Friends of Jesus help him?
3. How do churches help to carry on the work of Jesus?

WHEN YOU HAVE READ 'THE PURPOSE OF THE VENTURE: BREAKING DOWN ALL BARRIERS' (p. 28).

Drawing and Painting

Illustrate how Jesus cared for people, whoever they were, from three of the stories Dr. Luke tells us, and write out underneath, in your own words, what happened. Why didn't other people care for them?

Acting or Miming

Make a short play or plan a mime on one of these stories: 'A Roman Officer' or 'Lepers'. You could put the play on a tape-recorder and let the class listen to it; and then discuss how these stories help us to care for people. Who in your neighbourhood needs someone to care specially for them? Who is caring for them? Can *you* do anything to help them? Is anybody being neglected or ignored? And why? Are there any barriers between people which hinder help being given where it is needed?

Finding Things out

1. Read again 'The Stories of Jesus' (*The Message*, p. 31). Which of these stories (do you think) best shows us what makes us think wrongly of other people? Can you illustrate the story from anything that has happened in your own town or village?

2. What barriers are there between people in your town which stop them from understanding one another and being friends with one another? Who is trying to break these barriers down and doing something about it?

3. One of the great barriers today is the barrier of Race. People of different races find it difficult to live together and understand one another. What people of different races are there in your town? Who is helping them to meet together and understand one another? In some towns there is an 'International House' or 'International Club'. If there is such a place in your town, ask your teacher if you can invite its Warden to come and tell you about it.

Writing

Write down a list of the barriers that stop people today from understanding one another and make their living happily together difficult. Write out what you think people could do to break the barriers down.

When you have read 'The Cost of the Venture' (p. 34). and 'Not the End but the Beginning' (p. 43).

Drawing or Painting

Make pictures of these scenes: 'The Supper'; 'In the Orchard'; 'Jesus on Trial'; 'At Skull Hill'; 'On a Country Road'. You could add pictures of other stories, and make them into a frieze, or put them together in a book, and give it the title of 'Dr. Luke's Story of the Last Days of Jesus'.

Write a short description of what each story is about.

Acting or Miming

Make a short play or prepare a mime about one of these stories: 'In the Orchard'; 'The Women at the Grave'; 'On a Country Road'.

You could write a short play about a boy who was living in Jerusalem at the time, and tell the story of the last days of Jesus through his eyes. What would an ordinary citizen in Jerusalem see of these events?

Writing

1. Imagine you were one of the soldiers on guard at Pilate's headquarters. Write a letter home telling your parents about what happened that night, when Jesus was on trial, as you saw it.

2. Cleopas and his friend told the Friends of Jesus in the house all about what happened on their walk home. Write out the account you think Cleopas might have given them.

Models

See if you can make a simple model of the Temple and its courts with the Tower of Antonia.

Tape-recorder

1. If a play has been written, put it on the tape-recorder for the class to hear. *Or* put the soldier's letter or Cleopas's account (see 'Writing' above) on the tape-recorder for the class to hear.

2. Put a reading of 'Jesus on Trial' on the tape-recorder. One person can read the story, others can take the parts of Pilate and the crowd.

WHEN YOU HAVE READ ALL PART ONE

In Part One Dr. Luke tells us in his own words the same story which we have told, in Mark's words, in Volume One, *The Beginning*. Sometimes he used Mark's own words (I haven't given these stories here); sometimes he added to Mark's stories and made them fuller; sometimes he used stories and reports which Mark had not come across.

1. Here are some stories in which Dr. Luke has added information to Mark's account, or has given a different account:

'John the Hermit' (*The Beginning* p. 23; here, p. 18)

'Jesus hears God's Call' (*The Beginning* p. 25; here, 'Jesus hears God's Call' and 'Which Way?', p. 20)

'The Twelve' (*The Beginning*, p. 32; here, p. 26)

'The Supper' (*The Beginning*, p. 67; here, p. 35)

'In the Orchard' (*The Beginning*, p. 69; here, p. 38)

'At Skull Hill' (*The Beginning*, p. 73; here, p. 41)

'Jesus is Risen' (*The Beginning*, p. 75; 'The Women at the Grave', here, p. 43)

2. Here are some stories to compare together:

'In Bethany' (*The Beginning*, p. 65), 'A Woman who was "a bad lot"', (here, p. 31). Two stories about two women.

'A Jericho Beggar' (*The Beginning*, p. 55), 'A Chief Tax Collector', here, p. 33). Two Jericho stories.

3. Here are some stories which only Dr. Luke tells us:

'Peter', p. 24; 'The Seventy Two', p. 27; 'Martha and Mary', p. 28; 'A Roman Officer', p. 29 (look up Matthew 8.5–13 in your Bibles); 'Lepers', p. 32; 'On a country Road', p. 44.

Choose one story from each section above and illustrate what you find out in any way you wish. You can illustrate it by painting pictures, or acting or miming, or writing down what you have found out.

Twenty Questions

See how much you can remember of the stories of Part One. One of you can choose a person or thing from one of the stories; the others in the class can try to find out what you have chosen by asking questions, but only questions like 'Is it a man?', 'Is it made of cloth?' If anybody asks a direct question ('Is it Peter?') the game is ended—if he is right, he has won; if wrong, he has lost.

Part Two—Across the World

When you have read
'The venture begins again',
'Jerusalem City' and 'Palestine' (pp. 50–63).

Drawing or Painting

Make pictures of 'The Cripple at the Temple Gate'; 'Gamaliel speaks to the Jewish Council'; *or* 'Philip and the Officer on the Desert Road'.

Acting or Miming

Make a short play or prepare a mime about these stories: 'The Great Day'; 'Clash with the Jewish Leaders'; *or* 'Philip and Simon the Magician'. The short play could be put on a tape-recorder for the class to hear and discuss.

Writing

1. Write out in your own words what Peter said to the crowds on 'The Great Day'; *or* what he said to the Jewish Council.
2. There were no newspapers in those days. But imagine that there were and you were a newspaper reporter. Write a report for your newspaper about what happened on 'The Great Day'; *or* the trial of Peter and John.
3. Describe the way the Friends of Jesus lived in Jerusalem (p. 54), and compare it with what Jesus said about how his Friends should live (*The Message*, p. 66 and p. 82).

Talking

Imagine your class is the meeting of Christians in Jerusalem who had been waiting for Peter and John to come back from their trial. Let one of you be Peter and tell the others what happened at the trial (p. 57).

When you have read the stories about
Stephen, Peter and Paul in
'World Adventure: Everybody Matters' (pp. 64–81).

Drawing or Painting

Make pictures of 'Stephen facing his Accusers'; 'Peter on the flat Roof of the House'; 'Peter meets Captain Cornelius'; 'Peter escapes from Prison'; 'Paul sets off for Damascus'; *or* 'Paul escapes over the City Wall'.

Acting or Miming

These stories would make good short plays or mimes: 'Peter and Captain Cornelius'; *or* 'Paul in Damascus'. Put them on a tape-recorder, and let the class hear them.

Writing

1. Imagine you were the soldier Captain Cornelius sent to fetch Peter, and you were writing a letter home to your parents·just after it had happened. Tell them what happened.
2. Imagine that Ananias sent an account to Peter of how Paul became a Christian. Write out the letter you think he would have sent.

Talking

1. Imagine that your class is the meeting of Christians in Jerusalem who had been praying for Peter in prison. How do you think Peter told them what had happened? Tell the class (p. 75).
2. Imagine you were Paul. He has now got back to his native town of Tarsus. Tell the class what you think Paul said to his friends in Tarsus when he told them what had happened in Damascus and Jerusalem.

Finding Things out

1. Find out what the city of Damascus was like.
2. Find out what you can about the Roman Army—soldiers and officers, their dress and arms. The Grosvenor Museum, Chester, publishes a booklet *The Roman Army* with useful illustrations.

Drawing or Painting

Illustrate the six stories in 'From East to West'. See if your local Travel Agency has any leaflets about Greece and Turkey and Italy; these often have very good pictures in them.

Writing

1. Dr. Luke kept a diary. Imagine *you* had visited, with Paul, 'the Greek Island' *or* 'the Highlands of Anatolia' and had kept a diary. Write down, under the days 'Friday', 'Saturday', etc., *your* account of what happened.

2. There were no newspapers in Athens in those days. But imagine there were, and you were the editor of one of them. The editor of a newspaper writes an 'editorial' in which he discusses something which he thinks important or which he thinks will interest his readers. Write an editorial discussing Paul's meeting with the City Council. You can take the point of view of the members of the Council who thought Paul was just a 'chatterer'; *or* you can write as if you agreed with the members who said, 'We'll hear you again about all this'. (See how the editorials are written in the newspaper you take at home.)

3. Write an account of the stormy sea journey as told by the captain of the ship.

Maps

Make a map of the Mediterranean Sea and the countries on its shores; and put in the places discussed in both these sections. You can put in the sea routes and the roads people used and mark the course Paul's ships took, and the roads he travelled along.

Acting or Miming

Write a short play or prepare a mime on 'The Great Plan', *or* on one of the incidents in 'From East to West'. Remember Dr. Luke only tells about the most important things that happened; what else do you think may have happened before and after?

Finding Things out

Athens was 'the most famous Greek city of all', Rome was the most important city at the time. Find out all you can about these two great cities and their famous buildings.

Twenty Questions

See how much you can remember of the stories in Part Two. For playing the game, see 'Twenty Questions' on p. 108.

WHEN YOU HAVE READ THE WHOLE BOOK

This book tells how the Good News was taken from Galilee, in a far away province of the Roman Empire, to Rome, the capital city. The Good News is for everybody everywhere, and Jesus wanted everybody to hear it. So Dr. Luke's story does not stay in Palestine; it goes out to the cities of the great world beyond. It is the story of a bold, exciting and sometimes dangerous adventure.

Now you have found out what happened in the different places in Palestine and the world beyond it, try to see them all as part of one big story. Here are some things to do.

Drawing or Painting

1. You have already made some pictures of parts of the story. Can you make a frieze of them so that together they tell 'How they brought the Good News from Galilee to Rome'? You may have to add some more pictures to make them complete. *Or* you could arrange the pictures in a large book, and give it the same title. With each picture write a short account of what happened. Here are some headings for the frieze or for the chapters in the book: 'By Jordan River' (*or* 'Where the Story begins') (p. 18); 'In Galilee' (p. 29); 'Jerusalem'—this would need several pictures to show what Jesus did in the city, how he died there and how his Friends learned he was raised to life again, what *they* did in Jerusalem (p. 34); 'Samaria' (p. 60); 'The Desert Road' (p. 62); 'Caesarea' (p. 69); 'Damascus' (p. 78); 'Antioch' (p. 96); 'Cyprus' (p. 86); 'Anatolia' (p. 86); 'Athens' (p. 89); 'Malta' (p. 96); 'Rome' (p. 98).

Put your own titles on the pictures. Can you think of another title for the frieze or the book?

2. You could arrange the pictures you have made (and add to them to make them complete) to show all the different kinds of people who were told the Good News, whether they believed it or didn't. Look through the stories again and make your own list of people. The Jews divided the world into 'Jews and foreigners', just as the Greeks thought of 'Greeks and barbarians'. Jesus crossed the barriers. Let us see how his Friends crossed them. Here are some suggestions: 'Jews' (there were different kinds of Jews, remember—Galileans, Judeans, Jews who lived in foreign cities) (p. 52); 'foreigners' ('Greeks', 'Romans' and those who were 'natives' (as we might say) and did not have the right of citizenship) (p. 96). We could also divide them in other ways; educated and uneducated, country people and city people, men and women, rulers and those who are ruled by them, slaves and freemen, easterners (east of the Aegean Sea) and westerners; we could divide them by the countries they lived in, Africans, Syrians, Arabians, Greeks, Italians.

Arrange your pictures to show how the Friends of Jesus tried to break down all these barriers between people.

Acting or Miming

1. Make play with several acts in it to show how the Good News was brought to people of all sorts. Read through what I have written above, for those who like drawing or painting, about the different kinds of people living in the Roman Empire. Your play could show how the Good News came to city people and country people, to people who lived in the east and people who lived in the west, to Jews and Greeks and to people who weren't thought good enough to be proper citizens of the Empire. You could make Paul its hero, and show him meeting all these different sorts of people.

2. You could make up a play set in Rome where people from all over the world met. Make up a story about the Friends of Jesus there, many of whom had come from distant places. What had brought them there? Had they heard the Good News back in their home cities, and then, when they had got to Rome, found the house where the Friends of Jesus met, knowing they would be welcome there, whoever they were or where-

ever they had come from? Did some of them bring letters from the Friends of Jesus in their own home towns with them? You could make up a story of their meeting together on 'the first day of the week' in a house in a back street of the city.

3. Make a play about a sailor who sailed from port to port. He is a Christian, so when he lands at a port he tries to find the house where the Christians meet together. Suppose he sailed in a merchant ship between the mainland ports in the Aegean. He could sail from Ephesus, and call in at Troas, Athens and Corinth, and then back to Ephesus.

4. Make a play about a Christian soldier (like Captain Cornelius) who carries the Imperial Post along one of the great roads and meets Christians in the towns he passes through.

Models

Make a model of an Egyptian grain ship; a Greek Temple; *or* a Greek house, such as Christians used to meet in.

Stamps and Photographs

If you collect stamps, look up the stamps which the countries mentioned in Dr. Luke's stories issue today.

Maps

Make a map of the Roman Empire to show (1) the great cities of the Empire and the countries they belonged to; (2) places mentioned in this book where Jewish people were living; (3) all the places where Christians lived or which Christians visited. Show the main Roman roads (there were more than we have shown) and the shipping routes along which Christians travelled.

Show how the Good News spread across the world; link Galilee with all the places where Dr. Luke tells us Christians went.

Writing

1. Here is a letter (found in the dry sand of a village in Egypt) sent home by an Egyptian soldier to his father. He had joined the Roman Army and been given a Roman name in the port of Misenum, not far from the port of Puteoli where Paul landed (p. 98). His Egyptian name was Apion.

Here is the letter:

Apion to Epimachus, his father.

Sir, I hope you are well—and my sister and her daughter and my brother. I had a rough sea journey, but I arrived safely. When I got here to Misenum, I was given my pay—three pieces of gold. So I am all right. Do write me to tell me how you are and everybody else. I'll try not to let you down. Give Capilo my good wishes, and my brother and sister and Serenella [was she his girl friend?] and all my friends. I am sending with Euctemon a little picture of myself. I've got a new Roman name—Antonius Maximus.   The Athenian Regiment

P.S. Serenus and Turbo send their good wishes too.

Imagine you were a soldier like Apion; and you left your home in Antioch (p. 81), and joined your regiment at Misenum, as Apion did. But you were also a Christian, and hearing that there were Friends of Jesus at Puteoli, you went along there to look them up. You stayed with them before you went off with your regiment. Suppose your regiment was then stationed in Rome, and you find out where the Friends of Jesus there met. Now write a letter home to your father in Antioch telling him all about your experiences, and how you met Friends of Jesus in Puteoli and Rome.

2. Dionysius was an important man in Athens. He was a member of the City Council. He became a Christian after hearing Paul speak (p. 89). Imagine you are Dionysius and write down what you think he might have told his friends afterwards about what happened that day in the City Council.

3. During the two years Paul was in Rome, he must often have talked to the Friends of Jesus there about all that happened in the cities on the shores of the Aegean Sea. Suppose they said to him, 'Tell us what happened in Lystra' (p. 86); *or* 'Tell us again about the stormy journey you had' (p. 94). Write out what you think Paul would have said. (Remember Paul journeyed all the way from Palestine, and don't forget to say something about *why* Paul had been brought as a prisoner—he called himself 'a prisoner for Jesus'.)

4. Which of Dr. Luke's stories helps you best to see that the Good News is for *everybody*? Describe the story and write down why you chose it and how it makes this clear.

5. Compare the stories about Peter and Paul as Dr. Luke has told them. In what ways were Peter and Paul alike, and in what ways were they different?

Talking

Imagine your class is the meeting of the City Council in Athens (p. 89). Put in your own words what Paul said to the Council. *Or*, imagine your class is the crowd at Lystra (p. 86), and in the same way put what Paul said to the crowd in your own words. Ask your teacher if you can speak it to the class.

Flannelgraph

You can make a flannelgraph by using a large sheet of plain flannel or lint. Then you can draw and paint pictures of different people and objects (houses, trees etc.), cut them out and stick some flannel or lint on the back of each. They will then stick to the flannel background. You can build up your own pictures of scenes from Dr. Luke's stories. (Your art master or mistress will help you to make these.)

Tape-recording

1. The B.B.C. and I.T.V. often interview people. Imagine you were interviewing either Paul, the Governor (p. 86); or Silas (p. 88); or Dionysius (p. 89); or Dr. Luke himself. What questions would you want to ask, and what do you think the person interviewed would say? You would want to ask them how and why they had become Christians, and I am sure there are many questions you would like to ask Dr. Luke. Get other members to take part, and put the interviews on a tape-recorder and let the class hear it and discuss it.

2. You could interview people from different towns, and so show how the Good News is for everybody. The boy or girl who acts as the person interviewed must read the stories in which he or she appears very carefully and think about them.

Finding Things out

1. Find out what you can about Roman roads and how they were made and where they went; and the sea routes the ships took in those days. It was along these roads and sea routes that the Friends of Jesus like Paul took the Good News all over the known world.

2. Find out what you can about the Egyptian grain ships. Why did they carry grain and where did they take it? Read the story of the storm and the shipwreck (pp. 94–95); these will tell you something about these ships.

3. Find out what you can about different sorts of people who lived in the Roman Empire. You will find a lot of information about them in Dr. Luke's stories.

4. Most of the places mentioned in this book can be seen today and many of them are visited by tourists. Some of them are ruins, but many have become modern towns and cities. Find photographs of these places; note what they are like today and write about them.

5. Compare the two speeches Paul gave to foreigners at Lystra (p. 86) and at Athens (p. 89). How did Paul address different people in different ways?

6. How did the Goods News (Christianity) come to your town or village? How old are the churches and chapels there? When were they built and who built them? Who first brought the story of Jesus to your part of the country?

Twenty Questions

1. Find out, by playing the game Twenty Questions (see p. 108) how much members of the class can remember about Dr. Luke's stories.

2. Put a map of the Mediterranean Sea and its countries up on the wall; one of you can choose a person, the others can find out where he lived by asking questions ('Does he live in the East?' 'Does he live in a city?'). Play the game as you play Twenty Questions.

QUESTIONS TO DISCUSS

1. What sort of things keep people from mixing with one another, and make them have wrong ideas about one another? Can you illustrate this from what is happening in your own town or village?

2. Peter was a good brave man. Why do you think that it was not until he met Captain Cornelius (p. 69) that he really began to realize all that Jesus had lived and died for? Look up the stories 'On a Country Road' and 'A Mountain Walk' and 'In the Street' in *The Beginning* (pp. 49, 67), and 'The Supper' and 'In the Orchard' in this book.

3. If someone asked you 'What do you mean by "The Good News"?' how would you describe it? Discuss this in your class and see if you can agree just what you would say.

4. Why do you think Stephen, who had come to Palestine from overseas, saw so quickly what Jesus had lived and died for? Why do you think Peter, who had known Jesus from the earliest days, was so slow to see it? Do you think it had anything to do with living in an occupied country?

5. Jesus lived in 'God's Way'. How could you now explain, to someone who asked *you*, what 'living in God's Way' meant? What does it mean to people where you live? What ought it to mean?

6. Now you have read *From Galilee to Rome*, what stories about Jesus in *The Beginning* and what sayings of Jesus in *The Message* do you think make very clear that the Good News is for everybody everywhere?

THE SCHOOL ASSEMBLY

Ask your teacher if you can plan an Assembly Service, using readings from Dr. Luke's stories and helping the whole school to hear them. The stories need not be read by one person; you could have several persons taking the different characters. You could choose a hymn (a missionary hymn?) which fits the story, and write your own prayer.

HYMNS

1. Look through your school hymnbook (or your church hymnbook) and find the missionary hymns and hymns about the Christian Church. Can you find some *good* hymns which help us to realize that the Good News about God's love is for everybody everywhere? Who wrote them? When and where were they written?

2. Find hymns that have been written by people from countries other than your own; e.g. America, France, Germany. Can you find an Indian or Chinese hymn?

Where to find the Passages in your Bible